Ikenaga 2 Jos Leys

"A relatively simple formula can generate immensely complex images."– **Jos Leys**

Stories, Tables, and Graphs

Patterns, Functions, and Change

UNIT 6

Investigations

IN NUMBER, DATA, AND SPACE®

Glenview, Illinois • Boston, Massachusetts
Chandler, Arizona • Upper Saddle River, New Jersey

The Investigations curriculum was developed by TERC, Cambridge, MA.

This material is based on work supported by the National Science Foundation ("NSF") under Grant No. ESI-0095450. Any opinions, findings, and conclusions or recommendations expressed in this material are those of the author(s) and do not necessarily reflect the views of the National Science Foundation.

ISBN-13: 978-0-328-60025-0

ISBN-10: 0-328-60025-3

1 2 3 4 5 6 7 8 9 10 V003 14 13 12 11 10

Co-Principal Investigators

Susan Jo Russell

Karen Economopoulos

Authors

Lucy Wittenberg
Director Grades 3–5

Karen Economopoulos
Director Grades K–2

Virginia Bastable
(SummerMath for Teachers, Mt. Holyoke College)

Katie Hickey Bloomfield

Keith Cochran

Darrell Earnest

Arusha Hollister

Nancy Horowitz

Erin Leidl

Megan Murray

Young Oh

Beth W. Perry

Susan Jo Russell

Deborah Schifter
(Education Development Center)

Kathy Sillman

Administrative Staff

Amy Taber
Project Manager

Beth Bergeron

Lorraine Brooks

Emi Fujiwara

Contributing Authors

Denise Baumann

Jennifer DiBrienza

Hollee Freeman

Paula Hooper

Jan Mokros

Stephen Monk
(University of Washington)

Mary Beth O'Connor

Judy Storeygard

Cornelia Tierney

Elizabeth Van Cleef

Carol Wright

Technology

Jim Hammerman

Classroom Field Work

Amy Appell

Rachel E. Davis

Traci Higgins

Julia Thompson

Collaborating Teachers

This group of dedicated teachers carried out extensive field testing in their classrooms, met regularly to discuss issues of teaching and learning mathematics, provided feedback to staff, welcomed staff into their classrooms to document students' work, and contributed both suggestions and written material that has been incorporated into the curriculum.

Bethany Altchek

Linda Amaral

Kimberly Beauregard

Barbara Bernard

Nancy Buell

Rose Christiansen

Chris Colbath-Hess

Lisette Colon

Kim Cook

Frances Cooper

Kathleen Drew

Rebeka Eston Salemi

Thomas Fisher

Michael Flynn

Holly Ghazey

Susan Gillis

Danielle Harrington

Elaine Herzog

Francine Hiller

Kirsten Lee Howard

Liliana Klass

Leslie Kramer

Melissa Lee Andrichak

Kelley Lee Sadowski

Jennifer Levitan

Mary Lou LoVecchio

Kristen McEnaney

Maura McGrail

Kathe Millett

Florence Molyneaux

Amy Monkiewicz

Elizabeth Monopoli

Carol Murray

Robyn Musser

Christine Norrman

Deborah O'Brien

Timothy O'Connor

Anne Marie O'Reilly

Mark Paige

Margaret Riddle

Karen Schweitzer

Elisabeth Seyferth

Susan Smith

Debra Sorvillo

Shoshanah Starr

Janice Szymaszek

Karen Tobin

JoAnn Trauschke

Ana Vaisenstein

Yvonne Watson

Michelle Woods

Mary Wright

Note: Unless otherwise noted, all contributors listed above were staff of the Education Research Collaborative at TERC during their work on the curriculum. Other affiliations during the time of development are listed.

Advisors

Deborah Lowenberg Ball,
University of Michigan

Hyman Bass, Professor of Mathematics and Mathematics Education
University of Michigan

Mary Canner, Principal, Natick Public Schools

Thomas Carpenter, Professor of Curriculum and Instruction,
University of Wisconsin-Madison

Janis Freckmann, Elementary Mathematics Coordinator,
Milwaukee Public Schools

Lynne Godfrey, Mathematics Coach,
Cambridge Public Schools

Ginger Hanlon, Instructional Specialist in Mathematics,
New York City Public Schools

DeAnn Huinker, Director, Center for Mathematics and
Science Education Research, University of Wisconsin-Milwaukee

James Kaput, Professor of Mathematics, University of
Massachusetts-Dartmouth

Kate Kline, Associate Professor, Department of Mathematics
and Statistics, Western Michigan University

Jim Lewis, Professor of Mathematics,
University of Nebraska-Lincoln

William McCallum, Professor of Mathematics,
University of Arizona

Harriet Pollatsek, Professor of Mathematics,
Mount Holyoke College

Debra Shein-Gerson, Elementary Mathematics Specialist,
Weston Public Schools

Gary Shevell, Assistant Principal,
New York City Public Schools

Liz Sweeney, Elementary Math Department,
Boston Public Schools

Lucy West, Consultant, Metamorphosis:
Teaching Learning Communities, Inc.

This revision of the curriculum was built on the work of the many authors who contributed to the first edition (published between 1994 and 1998). We acknowledge the critical contributions of these authors in developing the content and pedagogy of *Investigations*:

Authors

Joan Akers

Michael T. Battista

Douglas H. Clements

Karen Economopoulos

Marlene Kliman

Jan Mokros

Megan Murray

Ricardo Nemirovsky

Andee Rubin

Susan Jo Russell

Cornelia Tierney

Contributing Authors

Mary Berle-Carman

Rebecca B. Corwin

Rebeka Eston

Claryce Evans

Anne Goodrow

Cliff Konold

Chris Mainhart

Sue McMillen

Jerrie Moffet

Tracy Noble

Kim O'Neil

Mark Ogonowski

Julie Sarama

Amy Shulman Weinberg

Margie Singer

Virginia Woolley

Tracey Wright

Contents

Investigations

Overview of Program Components

FOR TEACHERS

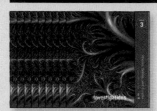

The **Curriculum Units** are the teaching guides. (See far right.)

Implementing Investigations in Grade 3 offers suggestions for implementing the curriculum. It also contains a comprehensive index.

The **Differentiation and Intervention Guide** offers additional activities for each Investigation to support the range of learners.

Investigations for the Interactive Whiteboard provides whole-class instructional support to enhance each session.

The **Resource Masters and Transparencies CD** contains all reproducible materials that support instruction. The **LogoPaths CD** provides an environment in which students investigate a variety of geometric ideas.

FOR STUDENTS

The **Student Activity Book** contains the consumable student pages (Recording Sheets, Homework, Practice, and so on).

The **Student Math Handbook** contains Math Words and Ideas pages and Games directions.

The *Investigations* Curriculum

Investigations in Number, Data, and Space® is a K–5 mathematics curriculum designed to engage students in making sense of mathematical ideas. Six major goals guided the development of the *Investigations in Number, Data, and Space*® curriculum. The curriculum is designed to:

- Support students to make sense of mathematics and learn that they can be mathematical thinkers

- Focus on computational fluency with whole numbers as a major goal of the elementary grades

- Provide substantive work in important areas of mathematics—rational numbers, geometry, measurement, data, and early algebra—and connections among them

- Emphasize reasoning about mathematical ideas

- Communicate mathematics content and pedagogy to teachers

- Engage the range of learners in understanding mathematics

Underlying these goals are three guiding principles that are touchstones for the *Investigations* team as we approach both students and teachers as agents of their own learning:

1. *Students have mathematical ideas.* Students come to school with ideas about numbers, shapes, measurements, patterns, and data. If given the opportunity to learn in an environment that stresses making sense of mathematics, students build on the ideas they already have and learn about new mathematics they have never encountered. Students learn that they are capable of having mathematical ideas, applying what they know to new situations, and thinking and reasoning about unfamiliar problems.

2. *Teachers are engaged in ongoing learning* about mathematics content, pedagogy, and student learning. The curriculum provides material for professional development, to be used by teachers individually or in groups, that supports teachers' continued learning as they use the curriculum over several years. The *Investigations* curriculum materials are designed as much to be a dialogue with teachers as to be a core of content for students.

3. *Teachers collaborate with the students and curriculum materials* to create the curriculum as enacted in the classroom. The only way for a good curriculum to be used well is for teachers to be active participants in implementing it. Teachers use the curriculum to maintain a clear, focused, and coherent agenda for mathematics teaching. At the same time, they observe and listen carefully to students, try to understand how they are thinking, and make teaching decisions based on these observations.

Investigations is based on experience from research and practice, including field testing that involved documentation of thousands of hours in classrooms, observations of students, input from teachers, and analysis of student work. As a result, the curriculum addresses the learning needs of real students in a wide range of classrooms and communities. The investigations are carefully designed to invite all students into mathematics—girls and boys; members of diverse cultural, ethnic, and language groups; and students with a wide variety of strengths, needs, and interests.

Based on this extensive classroom testing, the curriculum takes seriously the time students need to develop a strong conceptual foundation and skills based on that foundation. Each curriculum unit focuses on an area of content in depth, providing time for students to develop and practice ideas across a variety of activities and contexts that build on each other. Daily guidelines for time spent on class sessions, Classroom Routines (K–3), and Ten-Minute Math (3–5) reflect the commitment to devoting adequate time to mathematics in each school day.

About This Curriculum Unit

This **Curriculum Unit** is one of nine teaching guides in Grade 3. The sixth unit in Grade 3 is *Stories, Tables, and Graphs.*

- The **Introduction and Overview** section organizes and presents the instructional materials, provides background information, and highlights important features specific to this unit.

- Each Curriculum Unit contains several **Investigations.** Each Investigation focuses on a set of related mathematical ideas.

- Investigations are divided into one-hour **Sessions,** or lessons.

- Sessions have a combination of these parts: **Activity, Discussion, Math Workshop, Assessment Activity,** and **Session Follow-Up.**

- Each session also has one or more **Classroom Routines** and **Ten-Minute Math** activities that are done outside of math time.

- At the back of the book is a collection of **Teacher Notes** and **Dialogue Boxes** that provide professional development related to the unit.

- Also included at the back of the book are the **Student Math Handbook** pages for this unit.

- The **Index** provides a way to look up important words or terms.

Overview

Investigation	Session	Day	
INVESTIGATION 1 **Changes in Temperature over Time** Students read, describe, and represent the temperature graphs from different locations, including temperatures below 0° F. They match stories to temperature graphs by considering the overall shape of the graph and create original stories to match the shape of temperature graphs.	**1.1** Temperature Graphs Around the World	1	
	1.2 Changes in Temperature	2	
	1.3 Temperatures over a Day	3	
	1.4 Summer and Winter Days	4	
	1.5 Assessment: A Summer Day in Cairo, Egypt	5	
INVESTIGATION 2 **Cube Train Patterns** Students work with a repeating pattern of connecting cubes with a unit of red–blue–green. They determine the number sequences for each of the different colors in the cube pattern using what they know about multiples of 3.	**2.1** Cube Patterns: Red, Blue, Green	6	
	2.2 Where Are the Greens?	7	
	2.3 What Color Is It?	8	
INVESTIGATION 3 **Representing a Constant Rate of Change** Students work with a situation with a constant rate of change in a story context in which children receive a certain number of marbles each night. They use tables and graphs to represent and compare different situations and develop rules for describing the relationship between two variables (number of days and total number of marbles).	**3.1** The Marbles of Rhomaar	9	
	3.2 Working with Tables	10	
	3.3 Describing a Rule	11	
	3.4 Making Graphs from Tables	12	
	3.5 Using Graphs to Compare	13	
	3.6 What Do the Graphs Show?	14	
	3.7 End-of-Unit Assessment	15	

Each *Investigations* session has some combination of these five parts: **Activity, Discussion, Math Workshop, Assessment Activity,** and **Session Follow-Up.** These session parts are indicated in the chart below. Each session also has one **Classroom Routine or Ten-Minute Math** activity that is done outside of math time.

 Ⓦ Interactive Whiteboard

Activity	Discussion	Math Workshop	Assessment Activity	Session Follow-Up
Ⓦ	● Ⓦ			●
Ⓦ	● ●			●
Ⓦ	Ⓦ			●
● Ⓦ	Ⓦ			●
Ⓦ			●	●
●	Ⓦ ●			●
Ⓦ ●	Ⓦ			●
● ●	Ⓦ			●
Ⓦ ●	●			●
Ⓦ	● Ⓦ			●
Ⓦ	Ⓦ			●
Ⓦ	Ⓦ			●
●	Ⓦ			●
●	Ⓦ			●
			●	●

Ten-Minute Math

Today's Number	Guess My Rule
	Ⓦ
	Ⓦ
	Ⓦ
	Ⓦ
	Ⓦ
Ⓦ	
Ⓦ	
Ⓦ	
Ⓦ	
Ⓦ	
Ⓦ	
Ⓦ	
	Ⓦ
	Ⓦ
	Ⓦ

Mathematics

Stories, Tables, and Graphs is the Grade 3 unit in the Patterns, Functions, and Change strand of *Investigations*. These units develop ideas about patterns, sequences, and functions and are part of the early algebra foundation integrated into the *Investigations* curriculum.

LOOKING BACK

In the Grade 2 unit, *How Many Floors? How Many Rooms?*, students worked with ratio situations in two contexts: cube buildings and pattern blocks. Each cube building had a floor plan, and each floor of the building was identical. So a building with three cubes or "rooms" on one floor has a total of six rooms when a second floor is built on, and a total of nine rooms when the third floor is built on. Relationships between some of the pattern block shapes are also ratios: it takes three of the blue rhombuses to cover one of the yellow hexagons, six to cover two hexagons, nine to cover three hexagons, and so on. In both of these contexts, students built and recorded how one variable changed in relation to the other. Tables were introduced and used as a central representation for examining the relationship between the two variables.

Students also continued their work with repeating patterns from previous grades, associating the counting numbers with the elements in these patterns. Students described and compared the number sequences generated by a particular element in the pattern (e.g., 3, 6, 9, 12, . . . is the number sequence for the green cubes in a red-blue-green repeating cube pattern). Students' work throughout the unit focused on how and why different situations generate the same number sequence. For example, the same "counting by 3s" or "adding 3s" sequence is generated in several of the contexts.

Since the beginning of the year, students have been keeping a record of temperature. Making and interpreting their graph of temperature is part of the preparation for the work in this unit.

This unit focuses on 5 Mathematical Emphases:

1 Using Tables and Graphs Using graphs to represent change

Math Focus Points

- ◆ Describing the overall shape of a line graph—increasing, decreasing, staying the same
- ◆ Finding the difference between values on a line graph, including the difference between a positive and negative value
- ◆ Associating a story with its corresponding graph
- ◆ Plotting points on a graph to represent a situation in which one quantity is changing in relation to another
- ◆ Identifying points on a graph with corresponding values in a table and interpreting the numerical information in terms of the situation the graph represents
- ◆ Comparing situations by describing differences in their graphs

Through looking at temperature change over time in different places around the world, students learn more about making and reading line graphs—graphs that show a relationship between two variables. Learning how to find the two values represented by a point on a line graph by referring to the scales on the horizontal and vertical axes is an important skill; these conventions may not be obvious for students at first. In this unit, they have more experiences reading graphs; they also create graphs themselves to represent situations of change over time (in Investigations 1 and 3).

A central idea in this unit is learning to see a graph as a whole. For example, a graph of temperature over several months shows a great deal of variation over time. During the months of October and November, the temperature may go up and down many times. However, in the northern hemisphere, the temperature during these months in many places shows an overall downward trend. Through use of gestures, drawings, and the development of language about increasing, decreasing, and staying the same, students think about the overall shape of a graph and what that overall shape means. In Investigation 1, they encounter graphs that have a great deal of variation over time. In Investigation 3, they encounter graphs in which the rate of change is constant: the points on the graph fall in a straight line (see more below under Focus 3).

2 Using Tables and Graphs Using tables to represent change

Math Focus Points

◆ Using tables to represent the relationship between two quantities in a situation with a constant rate of change

◆ Interpreting numbers in a table in terms of the situation they represent

◆ Comparing situations by describing differences in the tables that represent them

Tables are another central representation in this unit to show how one variable changes in relation to another variable. As for any conventional representation, students must become familiar with these conventions through repeated use and, most important, through connecting the parts of the representation to the situation they represent. It is easy for students to get lost in the numbers in a table and lose track of what those numbers mean. If students see a column in which the numbers are 2, 4, and 6, it is easy for them to simply continue the pattern they see—counting by 2s. For example, in Investigation 3, students develop tables to represent a fantasy situation in which children receive a certain number of Magic Marbles each day. Tovar starts with 20 marbles and then receives two marbles each day. The beginning of a table showing the total number of marbles every five days for Tovar is as follows:

Day	Tovar
Beginning	20
5	30
→ 10	40 ←
15	50

Many students can continue the number patterns they see in the two columns, forgetting what the situation is that these numbers represent. Help students focus on individual rows of the table and ask them what that row tells them. For example, the row with the arrows shows that on Day 10, Tovar has 40 marbles. Looking at the relationship *between* the columns, not just within each column, is critical. Organizing data in a table and examining the relationship between columns of the table is one way to uncover a rule that governs the relationship between the two variables (in this case, number of days and total number of marbles).

3 Linear Change Describing and representing a constant rate of change

Math Focus Points

◆ Describing the relationship between two quantities in a situation with a constant rate of change, taking into account a beginning amount and a constant increase

◆ Creating a representation for a situation with a constant rate of change

◆ Comparing different representations that show the same situation

◆ Making rules that relate one variable to the other in situations with a constant rate of change

◆ Connecting the steps of a general method or rule to the parts of the situation they represent

In Investigation 3, students work with a situation that has a constant rate of change. On the fantasy planet of Rhomaar, children receive a certain number of Magic Marbles each day for the first 30 days of the year. For example, Franick receives three marbles each day for 30 days. In addition, some children have leftover marbles from the year before; Franick, for instance, has saved 30 marbles. This situation embodies a basic linear relationship. See **Algebra Connections in This Unit,** page 16. The total number of marbles can be determined by considering the starting amount (the leftover marbles), the rate of constant change (the number of marbles a child receives each day), and the number of days that have passed so far. This information can also be shown in a table or a graph.

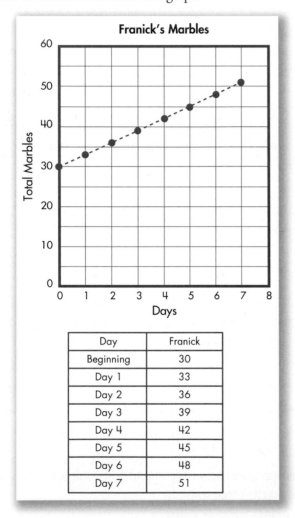

Franick's Marbles

Day	Franick
Beginning	30
Day 1	33
Day 2	36
Day 3	39
Day 4	42
Day 5	45
Day 6	48
Day 7	51

The values for such a situation fall in a straight line on a graph. For an amount of change in one variable, there is always the same amount of change in the other variable (e.g., when the number of days increases by one, the number of marbles increases by three).

A focus of this work is comparing situations with different constant rates of change. Students look at several kinds of comparisons in this context: 1) one child who starts with a smaller number of marbles than the other, but accrues marbles at a higher rate; 2) two children who start with the same number of marbles, but accrue marbles at different rates; and 3) two children who start with different numbers of marbles, but accrue marbles at the same rate.

4 Number Sequences Constructing, describing, and extending number sequences with constant increments generated by various contexts

Math Focus Points

◆ Identifying the unit of a repeating pattern

◆ Associating counting numbers with elements of a pattern

◆ Determining the element of an ABC pattern associated with a particular counting number

◆ Describing and extending a number sequence with a constant increment (e.g., 3, 6, 9, . . . or 2, 5, 8, . . .)

◆ Identifying numbers that are multiples of three, or one less or one more than a multiple of 3

Students should come to this unit with some experience of repeating patterns—patterns in which several elements are repeated in an unvarying sequence, such as, ABCABCABC . . . . Associating the counting numbers with the elements of a repeating pattern reveals important characteristics of the pattern and also provides an avenue into studying the number sequences themselves. For example, the counting numbers, starting with one, can be used to number a repeating pattern of colored connecting cubes.

As students work with this three-element pattern, they encounter three different "counting by 3" sequences. In this pattern, the green cubes are numbered by the sequence 3, 6, 9, . . . , the red cubes by the sequence 1, 4, 7, . . . , and the blue cubes by the sequence 2, 5, 8, ... Students figure out how each of the other two sequences is related to the multiples of three in order to solve problems about which color is associated with any number. For example, 29 is one less than a multiple of three, so the 29th cube is the second element in the three-element unit of the pattern and is, therefore, blue. In this work, students work on the idea of a general rule relating two elements (in this case, color and number in the sequence), an idea that becomes more explicit in Investigation 3, when they work with two related numerical variables in the marble context.

5 Measuring Temperature Understanding temperature and measuring with standard units

Math Focus Points

◆ Reading and interpreting positive and negative temperatures on a thermometer and on a line graph

◆ Associating temperatures with particular activities or clothing

Students have been recording and graphing temperature all year. Now they look back at their class graph to describe overall trends in temperature change. They read and interpret temperature values by comparing graphs showing temperature in different areas of the world, including negative temperatures. By relating negative values to temperature, students think through how to order negative values. Students also work on how different temperatures are perceived by people (hot, warm, cool, cold) through discussing activities and clothing that are associated with those temperatures.

Ten-Minute Math activities focus on

◆ Using evidence and formulating questions to make hypotheses about the common characteristics of numbers

◆ Systematically eliminating possibilities

◆ Using mathematical terms to describe numbers

◆ Generating equivalent expressions for a number using particular constraints

◆ Practicing computation skills

◆ Using notation to record expressions

LOOKING FORWARD In Grades 4 and 5, students will continue working with functions that can be expressed in a formula and functions that cannot be expressed in a formula (e.g., temperature or a graph of plant growth). For example, in Grade 4, students represent the change in the heights of plants over time that, like temperature, cannot be captured in a rule that determines future height. Students continue to study linear functions and to use tables and graphs to represent them. In addition, symbolic notation is introduced for writing equations that describe linear situations. In Grade 5, other kinds of functions that are not linear are introduced. In these situations, the rate of change is not constant; rather, the rate of change itself changes in ways that can be described mathematically. For example, as students consider the area of successive squares built with square tiles, they find that their graph of area related to side length is not a straight line.

Technology Note

Using the *LogoPaths* Software Students were formally introduced to the *LogoPaths* software in the 2-D Geometry and Measurement unit, *Perimeter, Angles, and Area,* the fourth unit in the Grade 3 sequence. We recommend that students continue to have access to the software **outside of math time** in order to return to *Feed the Turtle,* a *LogoPaths* activity, and to spend time with the *Free Explore* option. For information about the *LogoPaths* software and directions for *Feed the Turtle,* refer to the *Software Support Reference Guide* found on the CD. See **Part 5: Technology in *Investigations*: Calculators and Computers** in *Implementing Investigations in Grade 3:* Introducing and Managing the *LogoPaths* software in Grade 3.

Assessment

IN THIS UNIT

ONGOING ASSESSMENT: Observing Students at Work

The following sessions provide **Ongoing Assessment: Observing Students at Work** opportunities:

- **Session 1.1, p. 28**
- **Session 1.2, p. 36**
- **Session 1.3, p. 43**
- **Session 1.4, pp. 45 and 47**
- **Session 1.5, pp. 50 and 51**

- **Session 2.1, p. 59**
- **Session 2.2, pp. 63 and 66**
- **Session 2.3, pp. 68 and 69**
- **Session 3.1, p. 82**
- **Session 3.2, p. 89**

- **Session 3.3, p. 93**
- **Session 3.4, p. 102**
- **Session 3.5, p. 106**
- **Session 3.6, p. 110**
- **Session 3.7, p. 114**

WRITING OPPORTUNITIES

The following sessions have **writing** opportunities for students to explain their mathematical thinking:

- **Session 1.3, p. 42**
  Student Activity Book, p. 13

- **Session 1.4, p. 47**
  Student Activity Book, pp. 19–20

- **Session 1.5, p. 50**
  M20, Assessment: A Summer Day
  in Cairo, Egypt

- **Session 2.2, pp. 63–65**
  Student Activity Book, pp. 31–36

- **Session 2.3, pp. 68 and 72**
  Student Activity Book, pp. 38–39, 41

- **Session 3.3, p. 93**
  Student Activity Book, pp. 54–55

- **Session 3.4, p. 99**
  Student Activity Book, pp. 60 and 63

- **Session 3.7, pp. 113 and 115**
  M30–M31, M35–M36, End-of-Unit
  Assessment

PORTFOLIO OPPORTUNITIES

The following sessions have work appropriate for a **portfolio:**

- **Session 1.5, p. 50**
  M20–M21, Assessment: A Summer
  Day in Cairo, Egypt

- **Session 2.3, p. 68**
  Student Activity Book, pp. 38–39

- **Session 3.2, pp. 88–89**
  Student Activity Book, pp. 49–51

- **Session 3.4, p. 98**
  Student Activity Book, pp. 59–60

- **Session 3.5, p. 105**
  Student Activity Book, pp. 65–67

- **Session 3.7, pp. 113–115**
  M30–M36, End-of-Unit Assessment

Assessing the Benchmarks

Observing students as they engage in conversation about their ideas is a primary means to assess their mathematical understanding. Consider all of your students' work, not just the written assessments. See the chart below for suggestions about key activities to observe.

See the **Differentiation and Intervention Guide** for quizzes that can be used after each Investigation.

Benchmarks in This Unit	Key Activities to Observe	Assessment
1. Interpret graphs of change over time, including both the meaning of points on the graph and how the graph shows that values are increasing, decreasing, or staying the same.	**Session 1.2:** Temperature Differences **Sessions 3.5 and 3.6:** Using Graphs to Compare	**Session 1.5 Assessment Activity:** A Summer Day in Cairo, Egypt, Problems 1–3 **Session 3.7 End-of-Unit Assessment Activity:** Problem A, Temperatures on Two Days
2. Interpret temperature values (i.e., relate temperatures to seasons, to what outdoor clothing would be needed, and so on).	**Session 1.2:** Temperature Differences **Session 1.4:** Summer Days	**Session 1.5 Assessment Activity:** A Summer Day in Cairo, Egypt, Problems 4–5 **Session 3.7 End-of-Unit Assessment Activity:** Problem A, Temperatures on Two Days
3. Create a table of values for a situation with a constant rate of change and explain the values in the table in terms of the situation.	**Session 3.2:** Tables That Go by 5s **Session 3.3:** Using a Table to Compare	**Session 3.7 End-of-Unit Assessment Activity:** Problem B, Sophie's and Tom's Race
4. Compare related situations with a constant rate of change by interpreting the graphs, tables, and sequences that represent those situations.	**Sessions 2.2 and 2.3:** Examining the Red and Blue Cubes **Session 3.3:** Using a Table to Compare **Sessions 3.5 and 3.6:** Using Graphs to Compare	**Session 1.5 Assessment Activity:** A Summer Day in Cairo, Egypt **Session 3.7 End-of-Unit Assessment Activity:** Problem B, Sophie's and Tom's Race

Relating the Mathematical Emphases to the Benchmarks

Mathematical Emphases	Benchmarks
Using Tables and Graphs Using graphs to represent change	1 and 4
Using Tables and Graphs Using tables to represent change	3 and 4
Linear Change Describing and representing a constant rate of change	1, 3, and 4
Number Sequences Constructing, describing, and extending number sequences with constant increments generated by various contexts	4
Measuring Temperature Understanding temperature and measuring with standard units	1 and 2

Algebra Connections

This essay illustrates how the ideas your students engage in throughout this unit lay the foundation for algebra. Third graders can and do think algebraically. Part of the work of this unit is helping students learn to verbalize those thoughts. Such skills will provide the basis for making sense of algebraic notation when it is introduced in Grade 4. Consider the following vignette from a class working on the story of the Magic Marbles in Investigation 3, Session 4:

Teacher: Close your eyes and think about Jorad. She had 45 marbles from the year before and she got 3 Magic Marbles nightly. How could you figure out how many marbles Jorad had on the 10th day without figuring out every day from 1 to 9?

Arthur: 3 times 10, that's 30. I think that's right.

Teacher: So she had 30 on the 10th day?

Arthur: No, wait . . .

Beatriz: She had 45 leftovers.

Teacher: What are you going to do with those 45?

Beatriz: Add it to the 30. 30 plus 45 is 75.

Philip: Because she had 45 marbles from the year before.

Chiang: You could use a number line and skip 30, but you have to start at 45.

Elena: You start with 45 and you jump 3 for every day.

Kenji: I did it differently. You just times 3 by the number of days. Then at the end you add 45.

Teacher: Elena, how could we record your rule? Kenji, how would we record yours?

With students' guidance, the teacher records Elena's and Kenji's methods for finding the total number of marbles on any particular day.

45 marbles + (3 marbles per day × number of days)

(3 × days) + 45

These students are finding the relationship between two variables in a situation of change at a constant rate. When students graph these marble situations in Investigation 3, they see that the points on the graph fall in a straight line. Here is a graph of Jorad's accumulation of marbles:

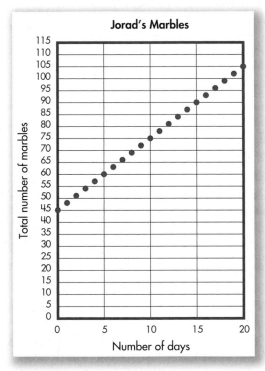

This situation is a *linear function*—that is, when the value of one variable changes by a certain amount, the value of the other variable changes by some other certain amount. For example, for any change of 1 day, the total number of marbles for Jorad increases by 3. This same change in the total number of marbles occurs whether the day increases from Day 2 to Day 3 or from Day 10 to Day 11 or from Day 29 to Day 30.

In Grade 2, students most often encountered linear functions in which the variables were related by a ratio. For example, they worked with the relationship between the number of "rooms per floor" (cubes in each layer of a building with identical layers) and the number of "floors" (layers) or the relationship between different pattern block shapes. In these situations, the variables are directly related by multiplication: if there are 5 floors and 4 rooms per floor, the number of rooms is $5 \times 4 = 20$: Number of rooms = 4 rooms per floor × number of floors.

In this unit, students encounter linear situations in which the variables are related by addition *and* multiplication. Let's look again at the example above. Jorad receives 3 marbles per day, but the relationship between the number of days and total number of marbles must also take into account the 45 marbles saved from the previous year. Students are learning to pay attention to both the starting amount and the amount of constant rate of change in order to relate the two quantities.

In articulating their rule as 45 marbles + (3 marbles per day × number of days) or as (3 marbles per day × number of days) + 45, Elena and Kenji are articulating representations of the relationship that approaches symbolic notation. They are moving from solving each problem separately to a general method expressed in shorthand by using words and numbers. "Days" or "number of days" is the variable that stands for *any number* of days. In the discussion, this sense of "any number" is apparent in the students' words. Although the discussion starts as a way to solve a particular problem—how many marbles does Jorad have on the 10th day?—the conversation shifts as students develop a more general method: "You just times 3 by *the number of days.* Then at the end you add 45."

In more conventional notation, in which *x* is used to represent the independent variable and *y* is used to represent the dependent variable, this equation could be written as $y = 3x + 45$, where *y* represents the total number of marbles and *x* represents the number of days. It is an example of the general form for linear functions: $y = mx + b$. The two numbers in this equation—3 and 45—have very different interpretations. The 3 represents the *slope* or the rate of change. In this situation, 3 is the number of marbles per day. The 45 represents a quantity that is not affected by the

value of the independent variable (the number of days). In this situation, this 45 represents the number of marbles Jorad saved from the previous year. We can think of this quantity as existing on Day 0, before the distribution of the marbles starts for the new year (a mathematical abstraction that helps us see the different parts of this equation). In this situation, when *x* (the number of days) has a value of 0, *y* (the total number of marbles) = 45. On the graph of this equation (see the figure above), the point (0, 45) is where the graph intersects the *y*-axis, and, for this reason, this value is called the *y-intercept.*

In this unit, students work on thinking through how the starting amount and the rate of change affect the function. When they compare the accumulation of marbles of two different children, they consider whether a child who starts out with fewer marbles will eventually "catch up" to a child who starts out with more marbles. For example, they notice that if a child with fewer marbles at the beginning accumulates marbles at a greater rate, that child will eventually have more marbles.

For most adults, notation (the use of variables, operations, and equal signs) is the chief identifying feature of algebra. The notation expresses in equations rules satisfied by particular pairs of quantities. Eventually, in later years, students learn to manipulate these equations in the abstract, disconnected from particular physical situations. Students' grounding in concrete contexts in the elementary grades supports their understanding of an equation such as the general linear form $y = mx + b$, and prepares them to understand how changes in the values represented by these symbols affect the mathematical relationships represented by the equation. In Grade 4, students are introduced to algebraic notation in a way that keeps it closely connected to a context with which students are working. By moving back and forth between the context, their own ways of describing general rules in words, and symbolic notation, students learn how this notation carries mathematical meaning. Students' *reasoning* about the mathematical relationship, *not* the notation, is the central work of elementary students in algebra.

Classroom Routines and Ten-Minute Math

The **Classroom Routines** and **Ten-Minute Math** activities, to be done in ten minutes outside of math class, are introduced in a unit and repeated throughout the grade. Specific directions for the day's activity are provided in each session. For the full description and variations of the Classroom Routines and Ten-Minute Math activities, see *Implementing Investigations in Grade 3*.

Activity	Introduced	Full Description of Activity and Its Variations
Classroom Routines: *What's the Temperature?*	Unit 1, Session 1.1	*Implementing Investigations in Grade 3*
Ten-Minute Math: *Guess My Rule*	Unit 2, Session 1.3	*Implementing Investigations in Grade 3*
Ten-Minute Math: *Today's Number*	Unit 2, Session 1.6	*Implementing Investigations in Grade 3*

What's the Temperature?

Students record the outside temperature every Wednesday morning on a chart and on a graph. They continue to practice reading charts and graphs, considering the relationship between them, and discussing changes in temperature over time.

Guess My Rule

Students decide, through careful observation and questioning, a "rule" that the leader established. The leader identifies specific numbers that do and do not fit the rule to get the game started. Students use this evidence to make guesses in order to deduce the rule.

Math Focus Points

◆ Using evidence and formulating questions to make hypotheses about the common characteristics of groups, people, or things

◆ Systematically eliminating possibilities

◆ Using mathematical terms to describe numbers

Today's Number

Students write several different expressions that equal a given number up to 500. They work with constraints that define the operations and the number relationships they can use, in order to practice and develop flexibility with computation skills.

Math Focus Points

◆ Generating equivalent expressions for a number using particular constraints

◆ Practicing computation skills

◆ Using notation to record expressions

Practice and Review

Practice and review play a critical role in the *Investigations* program. The following components and features are available to provide regular reinforcement of key mathematical concepts and procedures.

Books	Features	In This Unit . . .
Curriculum Unit	**The Classroom Routines** and **Ten-Minute Math** activities, to be done in ten minutes outside of math class, are introduced in a unit and repeated throughout the grade. Specific directions for the day's activity are provided in each session. For the full description and variations of the Classroom Routines and Ten-Minute Math activities, see *Implementing Investigations in Grade 3*.	• **All sessions**
Student Activity Book	**Daily Practice** pages in the *Student Activity Book* provide one of three types of written practice: **reinforcement** of the content of the unit, **ongoing review,** or **enrichment** opportunities. Some Daily Practice pages will also have Ongoing Review items with multiple-choice problems similar to those on standardized tests.	• **All sessions**
	Homework pages in the *Student Activity Book* are an extension of the work done in class. At times they help students prepare for upcoming activities.	• **Session 1.1** • **Session 2.3** • **Session 1.2** • **Session 3.1** • **Session 1.4** • **Session 3.3** • **Session 1.5** • **Session 3.5** • **Session 2.1** • **Session 3.6**
Student Math Handbook	**Math Words and Ideas** in the *Student Math Handbook* are pages that summarize key words and ideas. Most Words and Ideas pages have at least one exercise.	• **Student Math Handbook, pp. 42, 66–87**
	Games pages are found in a section of the *Student Math Handbook*.	• **No games are introduced in this unit.**

Differentiation

Supporting the Range of Learners

The **Differentiation and Intervention Guide** provides Intervention, Extension, and Practice activities for use within each Investigation.

Sessions	1.1	1.2	1.4	2.1	2.2	2.3	3.1	3.3	3.4	3.5	3.7
Intervention	●	●	●	●	●	●	●		●	●	●
Extension		●				●	●	●	●	●	●
ELL	●	●	●	●				●			

Intervention

Suggestions are made to support and engage students who are having difficulty with a particular idea, activity, or problem.

Extension

Suggestions are made to support and engage students who finish early or may be ready for additional challenge.

English Language Learners (ELL)

In this unit, students learn to interpret graphs that represent two variables as well as graphs that show change over time. Using temperature graphs and a fictional scenario about Magic Marbles, students practice reading and making graphs and tables, and discuss rules for extrapolating values in situations with a constant rate of change.

This unit also includes thematic vocabulary, such as expressions for describing weather, daily routines, and clothing, which students must understand and be able to apply in various situations. Preview relevant vocabulary and encourage students to practice using the words in one-on-one conversation or small-group discussions. You can also have students create thematically organized picture dictionaries, which they can use for reference during activities and discussions. Students will acquire much of this vocabulary through repeated exposure and practice.

As English Language Learners interpret tables and graphs, they might concentrate so hard on the numbers or on the language of the question or problem that they lose track of what the numbers represent. You can reinforce the connection between the numbers and their underlying values by asking guiding questions. **What does the 2 on this graph mean? Yes, 2 degrees. Is that hot or cold? In this row of the table, under Zupin, there's a 64. 64 what? Right, the 64 represents the number of marbles Zupin has on that day. Which day is that? Where do you see the number of the day when Zupin has 64 marbles?** By encouraging students to explain what the numbers represent, you can help them ground their mathematical knowledge in meaningful contexts.

Working with the Range of Learners: Classroom Cases is a set of episodes written by teachers that focuses on meeting the needs of the range of learners in the classroom. In the first section, *Setting up the Mathematical Community,* teachers write about how they create a supportive and productive learning environment in their classrooms. In the next section, *Accommodations for Learning,* teachers focus on specific modifications they make to meet the needs of some of their learners. In the last section, *Language and Representation,* teachers share how they help students use representations and develop language to investigate and express mathematical ideas. The questions at the end of each case provide a starting point for your own reflection or for discussion with colleagues. See *Implementing Investigations in Grade 3* for this set of episodes.

Mathematical Emphases

Using Tables and Graphs Using graphs to represent change

Math Focus Points

◆ Describing the overall shape of a line graph—increasing, decreasing, staying the same

◆ Finding the difference between values on a line graph, including the difference between a positive and negative value

◆ Associating a story with its corresponding graph

◆ Plotting points on a graph to represent a situation in which one quantity is changing in relation to another

Measuring Temperature Understanding temperature and measuring with standard units

Math Focus Points

◆ Reading and interpreting positive and negative temperatures on a thermometer and on a line graph

◆ Associating temperatures with particular activities or clothing

Changes in Temperature over Time

SESSION 1.1 p. 24	Student Activity Book	Student Math Handbook	Professional Development: Read Ahead of Time	
Temperature Graphs Around the World Students read and describe the temperatures, including temperatures below 0° (Fahrenheit), on temperature graphs from different locations.	1–5	66–69, 70	• **Mathematics in This Unit**, p. 10 • **Part 4: Ten-Minute Math and Classroom Routines** in *Implementing Investigations in Grade 3:* Guess My Rule • **Part 4: Ten-Minute Math and Classroom Routines** in *Implementing Investigations in Grade 3:* What's the Temperature?	
SESSION 1.2 p. 32				
Changes in Temperature Students describe the overall trends shown by the shape of a line graph. They find changes in temperature, including finding the difference between positive and negative values.	1–3, 7–12	71–72	• **Dialogue Box:** "The Shape Is Kind of Slanted", p. 143 • **Teacher Note:** Using Line Graphs to Represent Change, p. 117	
SESSION 1.3 p. 39				
Temperatures over a Day Students share methods to find the difference between a positive and negative temperature. They plot points on a graph to show the change in temperature over a day and describe the shape of the graph.	5, 7–9, 12–14	70, 71–72	• **Dialogue Box:** Temperatures Below Zero, p. 145	
SESSION 1.4 p. 44				
Summer and Winter Days Students match stories to temperature graphs by considering how features of the story match the overall shape of the graph. They create original stories to match the shape of temperature graphs.	15–21, 23–24	66–69, 70, 71–72		
SESSION 1.5 p. 48				
Assessment: A Summer Day in Cairo, Egypt Students complete and share stories that match the shape of temperature graphs. They complete an assessment in which they interpret the change in temperature over a day in Cairo, Egypt.	13, 19–20, 25–26	70, 71–72	• **Teacher Note:** Assessment: A Summer Day in Cairo, Egypt, p. 119	

Classroom Routines and Ten-Minute Math

See page 18 for an overview.

What's the Temperature?
- Mount the thermometer outside the classroom window
- Post the Date and Temperature wall chart and the Temperature graph in the classroom.

Guess My Rule
- No materials needed

Materials to Gather	Materials to Prepare
• **Classroom Temperature Graph** (from Classroom Routines, *What's the Temperature?*) • **Chart paper** • **T74 Temperatures from September to December Graph** 🖥	• **M6, Temperatures from Sept. to Dec. Graph** Make copies. (1 per pair, optional) • **M7–M8, Family Letter** Make copies. (1 per student) • **Discussion about three geographic locations** Spend time during social studies exploring the three locations used for temperature data: the North Pole, South Pole, and Honolulu, Hawaii. • **List of temperatures for Session 1.3** Keep in mind that you will need a list of temperatures for six times during the day in your location for Session 1.3. Plan how you will obtain these temperatures, either by reading your own thermometer or from an Internet site.
• **T74, Temperatures from September to December Graph** 🖥 • **T75, Temperatures over a Year Graph** 🖥	• **M11, Temperature Over a Year** Make copies. (1 per pair, optional) • **M9–M10, Family Letter** Make copies. (1 per student) • **Discussion about three international cities** Spend time during social studies exploring the three cities used for temperature data: Sydney, Australia; Tokyo, Japan; and Churchill, Canada.
• **T75, Temperatures over a Year Graph** 🖥 • **T76–T78, Temperatures over a Day Graphs** 🖥 • **Chart: "Graphing Words"** (from Session 1.2)	• **M12–M14, Temperatures over a Day Graphs** M12 has a temperature from 50° to 100°; M13 from 20° to 70°; and M14 from 0° to 50°. Select the page that contains the range of temperature for where you are and make copies. (1 per student) • **List of temperatures for a recent day** You will need a list of temperatures for 6:00 A.M., 9:00 A.M., 12:00 NOON, 3:00 P.M., 6:00 P.M., and 9:00 P.M. over the course of one day.
• **T79–T81, Summer Days: Graphs 1 through 3** 🖥 • **Chart: "Graphing Words"** (from Session 1.2)	
• **T82–T83, Winter Days: Graphs 1 and 2** 🖥	• **M20–M21, Assessment: A Summer Day in Cairo, Egypt** Make copies. (1 per student)

🖥 Overhead Transparency

Temperature Graphs Around the World

Math Focus Points

◆ Reading and interpreting positive and negative temperatures on a thermometer and on a line graph

◆ Associating temperatures with particular activities or clothing

◆ Describing the overall shape of a line graph—increasing, decreasing, staying the same

Vocabulary
temperature
degrees
negative

Today's Plan			Materials
① DISCUSSION **Temperature Where We Live**	🕐 15 MIN	👥 CLASS	• Class Temperature Graph (from Classroom Routines, *What's the Temperature?*); chart paper
② ACTIVITY **Temperature Around the World**	🕐 25 MIN	👥 PAIRS	• *Student Activity Book,* pp. 1–3 • T74 🖨 • M6* (optional)
③ DISCUSSION **What Do We See in the Graphs?**	🕐 20 MIN	👥 CLASS	• *Student Activity Book,* pp. 1–3 • T74 🖨 • Chart paper (optional)
④ SESSION FOLLOW-UP **Daily Practice and Homework**			• *Student Activity Book,* pp. 4–5 • *Student Math Handbook,* pp. 66–69, 70 • M7–M8, Family Letter*

*See *Materials to Prepare,* p. 23.

Ten-Minute Math

Guess My Rule   Choose the rule "Multiples of 3." Write three examples that fit this rule in a circle labeled: "Follows My Rule." Allow students to suggest numbers that may or may not fit this rule and place them inside or outside the circle. Encourage students to name the rule in any way they can. For example, "You name these numbers if you count by 3s." Can students think of larger numbers that are multiples of 3?

DISCUSSION

① Temperature Where We Live

15 MIN   CLASS

Math Focus Points for Discussion

◆ Reading and interpreting positive and negative temperatures on a thermometer and on a line graph

◆ Describing the overall shape of a line graph—increasing, decreasing, or staying the same

Briefly introduce the new unit, *Stories, Tables, and Graphs*. Let students know that they will look at graphs, tables, and patterns that show how different things change over time. They will describe and compare these changes. Sometimes they will make predictions about how something will continue to change. Students will study change in three contexts: temperature (with which they are already familiar from keeping the class chart this year), patterns made with connecting cubes (which they may remember from Grade 2), and a story about a strange planet on which students receive Magic Marbles. The unit begins with work on temperature in the students' own community and in other countries.

Since the beginning of the school year, you and your class have followed a routine to create a table and graph of the local temperature, and periodically students have discussed what they see in the graph. At the start of this session, return to the class temperature graph. This discussion should include questions of two types: (1) what the high and low points on the graph indicate about the temperature, and (2) the trends of temperature change, such as when the temperature decreased or remained steady for a period of time.

What can you tell about the temperatures since the beginning of the school year from looking at the graph? When were the temperatures the highest? When were they the lowest? Can you see when it started getting colder (or warmer)?

Follow-up questions to students' observations can include these:

What were the high and low temperatures?

What type of clothing did you wear outside in September? December?

What types of activities did you do when the graph was at the high points? At the low points?

In general, what was happening in September? October?

From the middle of October through December, what was happening overall? Even though sometimes temperatures went up and other times they went down, what was the general trend?

When did the temperature change the most? The least? How can you tell? What did that feel like when it changed?

As you continue to solicit responses and discussion, establish landmark temperatures with students by asking questions such as these:

At what temperature can you swim? Do you need a jacket? A heavier jacket? Do puddles freeze?

Record these landmark temperatures on chart paper for reference throughout the session.

Students look at the Class Temperature Graph to interpret the changes in temperature.

ACTIVITY

② Temperature Around the World

25 MIN   PAIRS

Ask students to look at *Student Activity Book* page 1 and show the transparency of Temperatures from September to December Graph (T74). ❶

Ask students what they know about these places and discuss where these places are located. Point out the locations on a world map and/or a globe. (Spend just a few minutes on this part of the discussion during math class. You may want to incorporate additional discussion during social studies.) Then focus on the temperature data.

What do you see in these graphs? Do any of these graphs look like our temperature graph? How are they similar and how are they different?

For Honolulu and the North Pole, ask students what they think the temperature is on September 1. Graphs in this investigation do not have gridlines for each degree, so students will have to estimate where the points fall between the marked values to determine many temperatures. Ask questions to help students learn how to read the temperature values.

Is it hotter or colder than 80 degrees in Honolulu on September 1? What do you think the line between the 80 and 90 stands for? Is the temperature in Honolulu hotter or colder than 85 degrees?

The South Pole has a negative temperature on September 1, presenting students with an added challenge. To help students describe this temperature, ask questions such as these:

On September 1, was the South Pole warmer or colder than the North Pole? Than 32 degrees? Than 0 degrees?

What do we call the numbers below zero? (negative numbers)

Do you think negative temperatures are warmer or colder than zero?

Is September 1 at the South Pole colder or warmer than negative 20 degrees? Than negative 30 degrees?

Stress to students that for some data points on their graphs, they may not be able to tell the exact temperature. Students' estimations may vary by one or two degrees, but that will be good enough to see how the temperature in each place is changing.

Math Note

❶ **The Temperature Data** The temperatures on *Student Activity Book* page 1 and other temperature data students encounter in this Investigation are actually the average temperatures for those dates in a recent year.

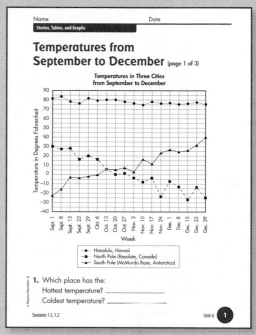

▲ **Student Activity Book, p. 1**

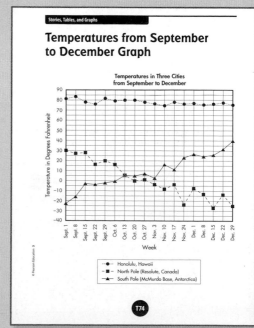

▲ **Transparencies, T74**

Name _____ Date _____

Stories, Tables, and Graphs

**Temperatures from
September to December** (page 2 of 3)

2. Answer the questions below about each city.

a. Honolulu, Hawaii
On which day was it the hottest? _____
Temperature: _____
On which day was it the coldest? _____
Temperature: _____

b. North Pole
On which day was it the hottest? _____
Temperature: _____
On which day was it the coldest? _____
Temperature: _____

c. South Pole
On which day was it the hottest? _____
Temperature: _____
On which day was it the coldest? _____
Temperature: _____

2 Unit 6   Sessions 1.1, 1.2

▲ **Student Activity Book, p. 2**

Name _____ Date _____

Stories, Tables, and Graphs

**Temperatures from
September to December** (page 3 of 3)

3. **a.** Choose one of the three
locations. Write it here: _____

b. What is an outdoor activity you would
do there?

c. During which months could you do your
outdoor activity?

d. Could you do your outdoor activity in one of
the other locations? Explain.

4. **a.** Choose another of these locations. _____

b. How are the temperatures from September to
December different from or similar to the
temperatures where you live?

Sessions 1.1, 1.2   Unit 6 3

▲ **Student Activity Book, p. 3**

Students work on *Student Activity Book* pages 2–3 with a partner. For each location, they determine the hottest and coldest temperature and the days on which these extremes occurred. Each student fills out an individual sheet after discussing their responses with their partners.

Students interpret changes in temperature around the world.

ONGOING ASSESSMENT: Observing Students at Work

Students find high and low temperatures on a graph, associate outdoor activities with temperatures, and compare temperatures.

- **Can students identify hottest and coldest temperatures and the dates they occurred from the graph?**

- **Do they identify appropriate clothing and outdoor activities for a given temperature?**

- **Are they able to estimate the temperature by using the marked gridlines?**

- **Do they associate negative numbers with colder temperatures?**

DIFFERENTIATION: Supporting the Range of Learners

Intervention If students need support interpreting the temperature graph, work with them in a small group to practice identifying the points and their values. Point to one of the dots on the graph and help students identify the date, the temperature, and the city represented by that point. Some students find it helpful to use two fingers to trace from a point down to the horizontal axis and across to the vertical axis to find the values for that point. Also, engage them in the opposite activity: specify a city and a date and ask them to find the temperature; or, as they become more proficient, specify a city and a temperature.

ELL Because English Language Learners might be more familiar with the landmark temperatures using the Celsius temperature scale, they might need extra support as they learn to use the Fahrenheit temperature scale. You can show students a table that includes landmark temperatures in both temperature scales, which will give English Language Learners the chance to demonstrate their knowledge of the Celsius scale. For further reinforcement, you might have students look up temperatures or study temperature graphs for cities in the native countries of the English Language Learners in the class.

DISCUSSION

3 What Do We See in the Graphs?

20 MIN   CLASS

Math Focus Points for Discussion

◆ Reading and interpreting positive and negative temperatures on a thermometer and on a line graph

◆ Associating temperatures with particular activities or clothing

This discussion covers the following three overlapping parts:

• Temperature values on the graphs for the three locations

• The types of outdoor activities and clothing appropriate for given temperatures

• Sharing estimation strategies for temperatures that do not fall on a marked gridline

Having worked with the graphs themselves on *Student Activity Book* pages 1–3 students will be able to offer more detailed analysis than in the earlier discussion. Throughout the discussion, raise questions comparing the temperatures of these international cities with temperatures in your own location.

Begin by posing questions about temperatures on the graph in relation to temperatures they know. Gradually move into questions about outdoor activities and clothing.

Math Note

❷ Talking About Negative Temperatures

Temperatures below 0° Fahrenheit, such as −20°, have negative values. These negative temperatures are commonly read as "minus 20" or "20 below zero." Students should hear these temperatures referred to as negative numbers (numbers less than zero) and should also become familiar with these other common phrases used to refer to these temperatures.

What is the warmest (coldest) temperature at the North Pole (South Pole, Hawaii)? Is it ever the same temperature there as it is where we live? If so, when? What would you be wearing? Can anyone imagine how cold that is? Would you want to go swimming then?

As students state their estimates for temperatures that do not fall on the gridline or are below zero, ask them about their strategies for estimation. Students may have different ideas about how to read temperatures below zero. Call attention to this.

[Kim] said that the coldest temperature for the North Pole is negative 32 degrees because it falls a little bit above the line for negative 30. [Kenji] disagrees and says that it's negative 27 degrees because negative numbers get larger as you keep moving farther away from zero. What do you think?

On chart paper or on the board, sketch a section of the *y*-axis from about 10° (Fahrenheit) to −30° so that it looks like a vertical number line. Some students may point out that it also resembles a thermometer. Ask students about these negative numbers:

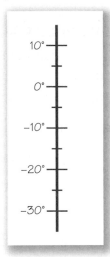

How are these negative temperatures similar to or different from positive temperatures? [Jane] says that the numbers are going up as we keep moving down, or that they're getting farther away from zero. Which is colder, 0 or negative 10? Negative 10 or negative 20? Have you ever felt a temperature that cold?❷

Throughout this investigation, continue to ground students' questions about negative temperatures in ideas about which temperatures are warmer or colder and how they are related to a temperature of 0°.

Students will need their completed *Student Activity Book* pages 2–3 for their work in Session 1.2.

SESSION FOLLOW-UP
4 Daily Practice and Homework

 Daily Practice: For ongoing review, have students complete *Student Activity Book* page 4.

 Homework: Students work on *Student Activity Book* page 5 for homework. Tell the class that for the next few days, they will be thinking about how the temperature changes over the day. Students will need their completed *Student Activity Book* page 5 for Session 1.3.

For the next few days, when you are near the window in our classroom, take a look at the thermometer. When you go home, is it colder or warmer than in the morning, or is it about the same? What about when you go to bed at night?

The homework page addresses the latter two questions. If students have a thermometer at home, they can record temperatures. If they do not, they can still write about when it is warmer or cooler, given what it feels like outside.

 Student Math Handbook: Students and families may use *Student Math Handbook* pages 66–69, 70 for reference and review. See pages 156–161 in the back of this unit.

Family Letter: Send home with each student a copy of Family Letter (M7–M8).

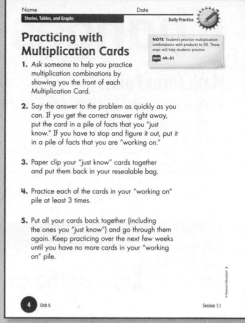

▲ **Student Activity Book, p. 4**

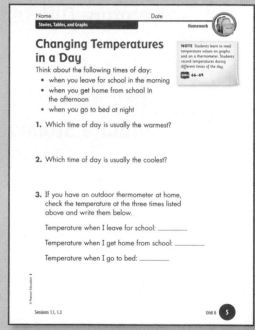

▲ **Student Activity Book, p. 5**

Changes in Temperature

Math Focus Points

◆ Describing the overall shape of a line graph—increasing, decreasing, staying the same

◆ Finding the difference between values on a line graph, including the difference between a positive and negative value

◆ Associating a story with its corresponding graph

Today's Plan		Materials
DISCUSSION ❶ **The Shape of the Graph**	15 MIN CLASS	• *Student Activity Book*, pp. 1–3 (from Session 1.1) • T74 • Chart paper
ACTIVITY ❷ **Temperature Differences**	35 MIN CLASS INDIVIDUALS PAIRS	• *Student Activity Book*, pp. 7–10 • T74 ; T75 • M11* (optional)
DISCUSSION ❸ **Temperature Stories**	10 MIN CLASS	• *Student Activity Book*, pp. 8–9 • T75
SESSION FOLLOW-UP ❹ **Daily Practice and Homework**		• *Student Activity Book*, pp. 11–12 • *Student Math Handbook*, pp. 71–72 • M9–M10, Family Letter*

*See *Materials to Prepare*, p. 23.

Ten-Minute Math

Guess My Rule Choose the rule, "Multiples of 5." Write three examples that fit this rule in a circle labeled: "Follows My Rule." Allow students to suggest numbers that may or may not fit this rule and place them inside or outside the circle. Encourage students to name the rule in any way they can. For example, "You name these numbers if you count by 5s". Ask:

• Why do the numbers outside the circle *not* fit?

• Can you think of larger numbers that are multiples of 5? Do you notice a pattern in the multiples?

DISCUSSION

① The Shape of the Graph

15 MIN   CLASS

Math Focus Points for Discussion

◆ Describing the overall shape of a line graph—increasing, decreasing, or staying the same

◆ Finding the difference between values on a line graph, including the difference between a positive and negative value

Students need their completed copies of *Student Activity Book* pages 1–3. Display the transparency of Temperatures from September to December Graph (T74) on the overhead projector. Start the discussion by asking about high and low temperatures.

Yesterday we talked about the temperatures at the North Pole and South Pole and in Honolulu. What did you find out about the high and low temperatures?

Next ask about the general trends and how the temperature changes over time in each location.

Now I want you to look at the graph of the North Pole and think about what it looks like. Who can show me with your hand how the graph goes? How about the graph for Honolulu? How would you say in words what happens to the temperature from September to December in Honolulu? At the North Pole? At the South Pole?①

Students use arm gestures to show general trends on graphs.

Encourage students to show with their hand or arm how the graph for the North Pole goes from upper left to lower right. Ask them what the

Teaching Note

❷ **Arm Movements** Teachers have found that when students use hand or arm gestures to show trends of graphs or parts of graphs, the gestures seem to help them visualize and describe these general trends. Remember that if you use any of the students' arm movements, you should face the same way as the students so that your movement goes in the same direction.

Professional Development

❸ **Dialogue Box:** "The Shape Is Kind of Slanted", p. 143

temperature would be at the upper left position (September) and then the lower right (December). Other students may draw a line on the board to show the general trend of the temperature change over time. Support students' understanding of the general temperature trend through using gestures, pictures, and language.❷ ❸

Construct a chart with the class that captures the shape and meaning of the three different general trends represented by the North Pole, the South Pole, and Honolulu. Title this chart "Graphing Words" and keep it posted as a reference in your classroom for the remainder of the Investigation. Use students' own language to describe the general trend for each place. Leave room below these three entries to add to the chart in later sessions. Your chart may look like the following:

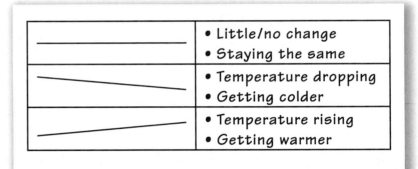

ACTIVITY

❷ Temperature Differences

35 MIN   CLASS INDIVIDUALS PAIRS

Introduce this activity by asking about temperature differences in Honolulu. Display the transparency of Temperatures from September to December Graph (T74) on the overhead projector.

Who can tell me what the difference in temperature is for Honolulu for the hottest and coolest days? [Keisha] says that the hottest temperature is 82 degrees and the coldest is 75 degrees. On the hottest day at 82 degrees, how many degrees colder does it have to get until it's the coldest day at 75 degrees?

Remind students that they are estimating temperatures, so each student may have a slightly different value for the hottest and coldest points. For Honolulu, the value should be around 83 degrees for the hottest temperature and 74 degrees for the coolest temperature.

Now students work in pairs for a few minutes to find the difference between the high and low temperatures for the North Pole and for the South Pole. After a few minutes, bring students back together even if everyone has not finished this task. Focus on the South Pole temperatures.

What is the difference between the warmest and coldest temperature for the South Pole?

This question may be challenging for many students because it involves finding the difference between a positive and a negative value. As in the previous session, use a vertical number line (similar to a thermometer) as a representational tool.

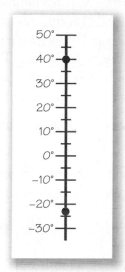

[Pilar] says that the hottest temperature is positive 40 degrees, and [Benjamin] says that the coldest temperature is negative 23 degrees. [Gina] disagrees and says that it's negative 22 degrees. It looks like it could be either because it falls between negative 20 and negative 25, so for this discussion we're going to say that it's negative 23.

Using the number line, ask students what the change in temperature is.

Students might say:

"I started at negative 23 and then counted back to 20, so I knew that was three. Then I counted by 10s to 40 and got to 60. I added the three back on and that's how I got my answer 63."

"I got my answer a different way. I started at zero. I knew zero to 40 was 40 and then zero down to minus 23 was just 23, so I added 40 and 23 and got 63."

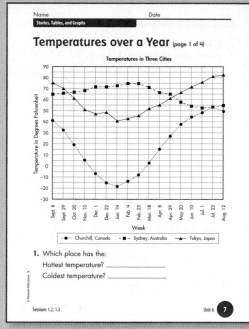

▲ **Student Activity Book, p. 7**

▲ **Student Activity Book, pp. 8–9**

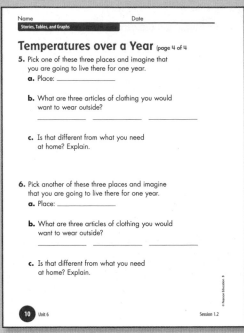

▲ Student Activity Book, p. 10

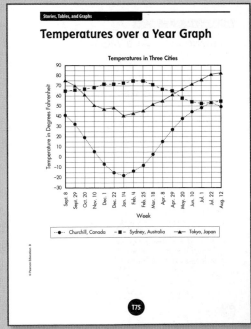

▲ Transparencies, T75

These ideas will be further explored when students consider the temperature in Churchill, Canada, in Session 1.3.

To introduce *Student Activity Book* pages 7–10, briefly ask students what they know about Sydney, Australia; Tokyo, Japan; and Churchill, Canada. This discussion should take just a minute or two. You may want to spend more time locating and discussing these places during social studies.

Sydney is the largest city in Australia, Tokyo is the capital of Japan, and Churchill is a small town in central northern Canada known as the polar bear capital of the world.

Display the transparency of Temperatures over a Year Graph (T75) on the overhead projector. Let students know that the graph on *Student Activity Book* page 7 displays temperatures for an entire year, from September to August, for Sydney, Tokyo, and Churchill. Help students identify which months of this graph match the class temperature graph, which goes only from the beginning of the school year until now.

Students work individually or in pairs to answer the questions on *Student Activity Book* pages 8–10.

Students should finish Problems 2, 3, and 4 on *Student Activity Book* pages 8–9 for a discussion in Session 1.3.

ONGOING ASSESSMENT: Observing Students at Work

Students determine the highest and lowest temperatures for the three cities represented on the graph and find the differences between the high and low for each city.

- **Can students identify hottest and coldest temperatures and the dates they occurred from the graph?**

- **Can students find the difference between the hottest and coldest temperatures, including between a positive and negative value?**

- **Are students able to estimate temperatures that do not fall directly on marked gridlines?**

- **Do students select appropriate clothing and outdoor activities for given temperatures?**

As students are working, look for several different approaches to finding the difference between high and low temperatures for

Churchill that could be shared in the next session. In particular, look for any representations students are using that you think will be helpful for the whole class to consider.**❹ ❺**

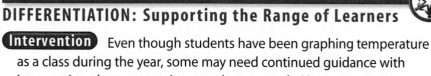

DIFFERENTIATION: Supporting the Range of Learners

Intervention Even though students have been graphing temperature as a class during the year, some may need continued guidance with interpreting change over time graphs accurately. You may want to meet with these students in a small group before the activity to review how to read the values on a graph. Ask them to talk through the story of the temperature change in just one of the cities from Sept. 8 to Aug. 12. Then talk through the story of the second city. At that point, many students may be ready to work on their own. For examples, see the following Temperature Stories discussion.

Extension Students who finish early can work on Problems 5 and 6 on *Student Activity Book* page 10.

DISCUSSION

❸ Temperature Stories

10 MIN   CLASS

Math Focus Points for Discussion

◆ Describing the overall shape of a line graph—increasing, decreasing, or staying the same

◆ Finding the difference between values on a line graph, including the difference between a positive and negative value

◆ Associating a story with its corresponding graph

Students should have *Student Activity Book* page 7 in front of them. Display the transparency Temperatures over a Year Graph (T75) on the overhead projector. Tell a story that fits the temperature of Sydney. Have students listen to your story, and then make a guess about the location to which the story refers.

In September, I decide to go for a walk outside. It is a little cool outside, so I need my jacket. Over the next several weeks, the temperature continues to rise. In January, my family and I have a picnic outside. I put on a pair of shorts and a shirt, pack up a lunch, and have a very nice time outdoors with my family all afternoon. Shortly after this, the temperature starts to go down and down. By the time June arrives, I need my jacket again when I go outside. Where am I?**❻**

Math Note

❹ Two Points at the Same Location on a Graph Many students are at first surprised that two points can occupy the same location on the grid and are not sure how to interpret these data. On July 22, the temperature is the same, about 53°, in Churchill and Sydney. If you notice that students are puzzled, talk through this situation with them. Could there be two places that have the same temperature on the same day? How would that look on the graph? Focus on the temperature data for one city at a time; trace with a finger along the Churchill temperatures from Sept. 8 to Aug. 12 and then along the Sydney temperatures, and help students compare the temperatures on July 1, July 22, and August 12. What happens in each city?

Professional Development

❺ Teacher Note: Using Line Graphs to Represent Change, p. 117

Differentiation

❻ English Language Learners You might need to preview clothing vocabulary with English Language Learners before they hear the temperature stories. You can show actual examples of each type of clothing and have students record the words in self-made picture dictionaries. As you discuss the clothing, use common weather-related vocabulary such as *warm, hot, cool,* and *cold.* It's *cold* outside. [Ines], can you choose a piece of clothing to wear when it's cold? Great, you chose *mittens.* [Kenji], can you find something else to wear when it's cold? Yes, a *hat* would be nice. After you introduce each word, have students add it to their picture dictionaries to help them later when they write their own temperature stories

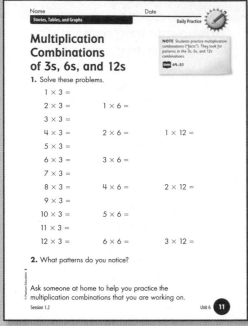

▲ **Student Activity Book, p. 11**

As students identify the place that fits the temperature story, ask them what in the story gave them a clue. They may tell you that it was warm enough to go for a picnic in January, or that the temperature slowly increased from September until January. If time permits, tell a similar story for Churchill, Canada. Ask students to again find clues in the story that tells them which location to pick.

It's September in my location. I need a jacket, but not my heaviest jacket. For the next several weeks, the temperature slowly goes down. By the time November arrives, the ground is covered with snow. I need to wear a heavier jacket so that I don't catch a cold. The temperature goes down even more! In January and February, it is so cold outside that it actually hurts to breathe. I can go outside for only a few minutes, and when I do I have to wear a big heavy jacket, heavy boots with many socks, heavy gloves, and a hat that covers all of my head. I get back inside as fast as I can. Over the next few months, the temperature slowly increases, but the snow doesn't start to melt until May or June. Where am I?

▲ **Student Activity Book, p. 12**

SESSION FOLLOW-UP

Daily Practice and Homework

 Daily Practice: For ongoing review, have students complete *Student Activity Book* page 11.

 Homework: Students complete *Student Activity Book* page 12 for homework. On this page, students record the high and low temperatures for the day in their own community. Session 1.3 will begin with students' completed *Student Activity Book* page 5 (from the homework for Session 1.1) and *Student Activity Book* page 12.

 Student Math Handbook: Students and families may use *Student Math Handbook* pages 71–72 for reference and review. See pages 156–161 in the back of this unit.

Family Letter: Send home with each student a copy of Family Letter (M9–M10).

Temperatures over a Day

Math Focus Points

◆ Plotting points on a graph to represent a situation in which one quantity is changing in relation to another

◆ Describing the overall shape of a line graph—increasing, decreasing, staying the same

◆ Finding the difference between values on a line graph, including the difference between a positive and negative value

Vocabulary

horizontal axis
vertical axis

Today's Plan		Materials
DISCUSSION **① Changes in Temperature**	25 MIN CLASS	• *Student Activity Book,* pp. 8–9 (from Session 1.2) • T75 • Chart: "Graphing Words" (from Session 1.2)
ACTIVITY **② Temperatures over a Day**	35 MIN CLASS PAIRS	• *Student Activity Book,* pp. 5 (from Session 1.1), 12–13 • M12–M14*; T76–T78 • Chart: "Graphing Words" (from Session 1.2)
SESSION FOLLOW-UP **③ Daily Practice**		• *Student Activity Book,* p. 14 • *Student Math Handbook,* pp. 70, 71–72

*See *Materials to Prepare,* p. 23.

Ten-Minute Math

Guess My Rule   Choose the rule, "Factors of 24." Write four examples that fit this rule in a circle labeled "Follows My Rule" (e.g., 1, 3, 6, 8). Allow students to suggest numbers that may or may not fit this rule and place them inside or outside the circle. Encourage students to name the rule in any way they can; for example, "They're all numbers that you can count by to land on 24."

DISCUSSION

① Changes in Temperature

25 MIN   CLASS

Math Focus Points for Discussion

◆ Finding the difference between values on a line graph, including the difference between a positive and negative value

◆ Describing the overall shape of a line graph—increasing, decreasing, or staying the same

Students need their completed *Student Activity Book* pages 8–9. Display the transparency Temperatures over a Year Graph (T75) on the overhead projector. Briefly review the high and low temperatures students found for each city. Then ask the class how they answered the questions about the differences in temperatures for each city. First ask students about Sydney or Tokyo. As needed, use these questions to review reading values for the points on the graph. If some students had difficulty understanding how two points can be at the same location on July 22, you can ask students to explain their ideas about how to interpret these points.

Then focus on Churchill. Ask what the high and low temperatures are for Churchill and sketch them on a vertical number line.

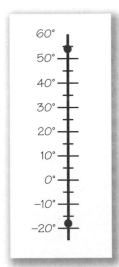

How did you find the difference between the high and low temperatures for Churchill, Canada? [Elena] said that this was challenging because the lowest temperature was a negative number. Who has a method they can explain?

Make sure that several different approaches are shared.

Students might say:

"I started at minus 10 and I counted by 10s up to 50—10, 20, 30, 40, 50. Then I had to add on the extra below minus 10 and the extra above 50, so that was plus 4 and plus 8. It's 72 degrees in all."

"First I knew that from 0 down to negative 18, that's just 18. And from 0 up to 54 is 54. So then I had to add 54 and 18. I did that in my head—54 and 10 is 64, then 6 more is 70, then plus 2. I agree with Philip—it's 72."

Ask students to demonstrate their methods on the vertical number line. ❶

Sum up this part of the discussion by asking these questions:

In which location is there the *most* change in temperature during the year? How do you know?

Refer back to the "Graphing Words" chart. Ask students whether they need to add other shapes to the class chart in order to capture the trends for Sydney, Tokyo, and Churchill. The additions to the table may look like the following:

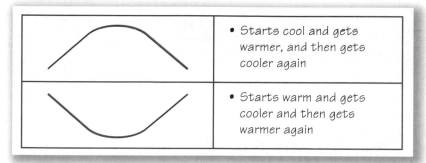

ACTIVITY

2 Temperatures over a Day

35 MIN | CLASS | PAIRS

This activity shifts the Investigation's focus from looking at the change in temperature over a period of months to looking at the change over a day. Students need their completed *Student Activity Book* page 5 and *Student Activity Book* page 12. Introduce this activity by asking what they found out.

For homework over the past couple of nights, you thought about what

Professional Development

❶ **Dialogue Box:** Temperatures Below Zero, p. 145

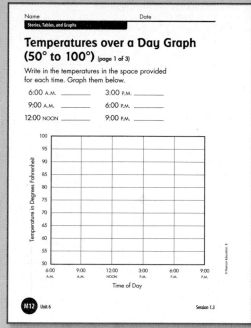

▲ **Resource Masters, M12; T76**

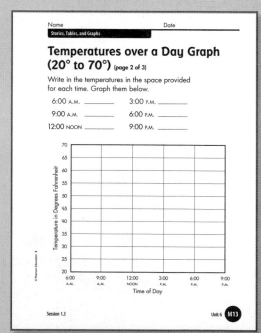

▲ **Resource Masters, M13; T77**

Temperatures over a Day Graph
(0° to 50°) (page 3 of 3)

Write in the temperatures in the space provided
for each time. Graph them below.

6:00 A.M. _____   3:00 P.M. _____

9:00 A.M. _____   6:00 P.M. _____

12:00 NOON _____   9:00 P.M. _____

Temperature in Degrees Fahrenheit

50
45
40
35
30
25
20
15
10
5
0

6:00 A.M.   9:00 A.M.   12:00 NOON   3:00 P.M.   6:00 P.M.   9:00 P.M.

Time of Day

M14   Unit 6   Session 1.3

▲ **Resource Masters, M14; T78**

Temperatures over a Day

Use your Temperatures over a Day graph to answer
the following questions.

1. On your graph, write what is happening to the
temperature above each part of the line that
shows the temperature change. You can use
these phrases:

Getting warmer   Getting cooler   Staying the same

2. Describe the shape of the line graph.
What does it tell you about this day?

3. How much did the temperature change from
9:00 A.M. to 12:00 NOON?

4. How much did the temperature change from
12:00 NOON to 3:00 P.M.?

5. What is the difference between the highest and
lowest temperatures of the day?

Show how you found the difference.

Session 1.3   Unit 6   13

▲ **Student Activity Book, p. 13**   *WRITING*

the temperature is like when you leave for school, when you get home from school, and when you go to bed. Some of you may have found the actual temperatures if you had an outside thermometer at home, looked it up in the newspaper, or heard it on the news. Who can describe what you found out about the temperatures at these times? When was it coolest? Warmest?

After a few responses about trends in temperature over a day, ask students to describe the temperature for the day by using gestures, by drawing on the board, or by using the words and phrases on the "Graphing Words" chart.

Students demonstrate temperature trends by drawing them on the board.

When was the temperature dropping? When was the temperature rising? Did it ever stay the same? Imagine what yesterday's temperatures would look like on a graph. What do you predict the shape of the graph will look like? Why?

Present to the class your prepared list of one day's temperatures for 6:00 A.M., 9:00 A.M., 12:00 NOON, 3:00 P.M., 6:00 P.M., and 9:00 P.M. Display the transparency of Temperatures over a Day Graph (T76–T78), with temperatures on the *y*-axis appropriate for your region. Give students a copy of the corresponding page from Temperatures over a Day Graph (M12–M14).

Ask students to identify the two axes and their properties.

What do the two axes represent? (time and temperature in degrees Fahrenheit)

Where on the horizontal axis is morning? Afternoon? Night?

Where on the vertical axis is it cooler? Warmer?

Where on the vertical axis is a temperature for which you would need a jacket?

Where on the vertical axis is a temperature when you'd be able to swim?

Plot the first one or two points with the class (6:00 A.M. and 9:00 A.M.), and lead them through plotting at least one or two more points. Students then complete the Temperatures over a Day Graph (M12–M14) by plotting the rest of the points and connecting the points with a line indicating how the temperature changed. When the graph is complete, students answer the questions on *Student Activity Book* page 13.❷

ONGOING ASSESSMENT: Observing Students at Work

Students plot points on a graph to show changing temperatures over a day. They answer questions about the shape of the graph and calculate differences between temperatures.

- **Can students describe how the temperature is changing for parts of the day and for the day as a whole?**

- **Can students identify hottest and coldest temperatures from the graph?**

- **Can students find the difference between two temperatures?**

Although students have been plotting points on a temperature graph as a class all year, creating their own graph by themselves is new. Support students to understand the conventions of this kind of graph, and assure them that all the lines and values can at first be confusing.❸

SESSION FOLLOW-UP

Daily Practice

Daily Practice: For ongoing review, have students complete *Student Activity Book* page 14.

Student Math Handbook: Students and families may use *Student Math Handbook* pages 70, 71–72 for reference and review. See pages 156–161 in the back of this unit.

❷ **Values Between Data Points** As temperature changes from one value to another, it passes through all the values between those two points. Although we do not know exactly how the change happened between the known points, students can make a reasonable guess about how the temperature changed in order to connect the points for which they do know the actual temperatures.

Professional Development

❸ **Teacher Note:** Using Line Graphs to Represent Change, p. 117

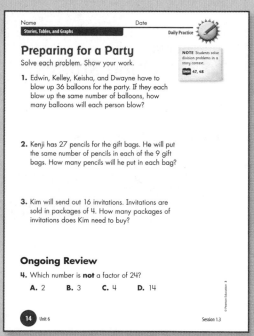

▲ **Student Activity Book, p. 14**

Summer and Winter Days

Math Focus Points

◆ Reading and interpreting positive and negative temperatures on a thermometer and on a line graph

◆ Describing the overall shape of a line graph—increasing, decreasing, staying the same

◆ Associating a story with its corresponding graph

Today's Plan		Materials
1 ACTIVITY **Summer Days** — 25 MIN / PAIRS		• *Student Activity Book,* pp. 15–18 • Chart: "Graphing Words" (from Session 1.2)
2 DISCUSSION **Matching Stories** — 15 MIN / CLASS		• *Student Activity Book,* pp. 15–18 • T79–T81
3 ACTIVITY **Winter Days** — 20 MIN / PAIRS		• *Student Activity Book,* pp. 19–20
4 SESSION FOLLOW-UP **Daily Practice and Homework**		• *Student Activity Book,* pp. 21, 23–24 • *Student Math Handbook,* pp. 66–69, 70, 71–72

Ten-Minute Math

Guess My Rule Choose the rule "Multiples of 10." Write three examples that fit this rule in a circle labeled: "Follows My Rule." Allow students to suggest numbers that may or may not fit this rule and place them inside or outside the circle. Encourage students to name the rule in any way they can; for example, "You name these numbers if you count by 10s." If students suggest a rule such as, "They are all even numbers," acknowledge that this is true but ask them to be more specific and notice that some even numbers are *outside* the circle.

ACTIVITY

① Summer Days

25 MIN   PAIRS

Students work in pairs to determine the story that matches each graph on *Student Activity Book* page 15 and *Student Activity Book* pages 16–18. ❶

After students have matched the three stories, they answer the questions for each graph and write graphing terms on appropriate parts of each of the three graphs:

Getting warmer

Getting colder

Staying the same

Explain to students that they should write these phrases along sections of the temperature graph that show these trends.

✔ ONGOING ASSESSMENT: Observing Students at Work

Students match stories and graphs by interpreting the trends of temperature change over the course of a day.

- **Are students able to identify qualitative descriptions (hot, cool) with approximate temperatures?**

- **Do students use the descriptions of temperature change in the stories to identify the corresponding graphs?**

✳ DIFFERENTIATION: Supporting the Range of Learners

Intervention Some students may benefit from talking through each story in a small group. As students read the stories, ask them to pause after each statement and imagine what this might look like on a graph. For some it may be helpful to underline the clues in the story that correspond to the changes in temperature and trace the matching graph section.

ELL You can support English Language Learners by previewing some of the daily routine expressions used in this activity. Make a chart showing various times of the day and have students discuss what activities they do at each time (e.g., *I wake up at 7:00 A.M.; I leave school at 3:00 P.M.*). Model the relevant language as necessary. Then have students label the activities next to the times of day on one of the graphs. Encourage English Language Learners to use this graph as a reference while you ask time- and weather-related questions.

[Dwayne], what time do you *wake* up? When you woke up this morning, was it *cooler* or *warmer* than it is now?

Teaching Note

❶ **Summer Days Graphs** Thursday's story goes with Graph 3, Friday's story with Graph 2, and Saturday's story with Graph 1.

▲ **Student Activity Book, p. 15**

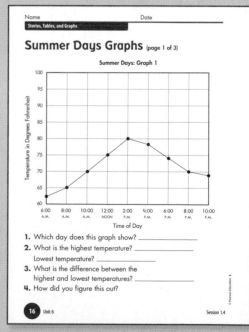

▲ **Student Activity Book, p. 16; Transparencies, T79**

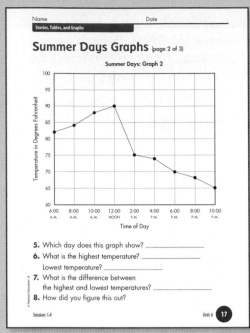

▲ **Student Activity Book, p. 17;**
Transparencies, T80

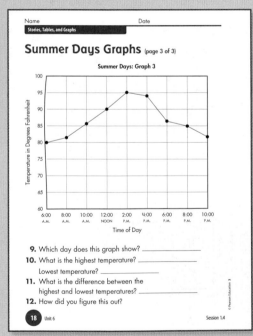

▲ **Student Activity Book, p. 18;**
Transparencies, T81

15 MIN CLASS

DISCUSSION

② Matching Stories

Math Focus Points for Discussion

◆ Describing the overall shape of a line graph—increasing, decreasing, or staying the same

◆ Associating a story with its corresponding graph

Students do not need to complete all the questions on *Student Activity Book* pages 16–18 before the discussion. Have students look at *Student Activity Book* page 15. Ask a student to read the story for Thursday, and then have another student paraphrase the story.

When you hear that story about Thursday, what did you think to look for in the graph to find which one matches? Which of these graphs shows what happened on Thursday? (*Graph 3*) **How do you know?**

Display the transparency of Summer Days: Graph 3 (T81).

Ask students what phrases and gestures they would use to describe different parts of the graph. As you move on to a new day, start with the graph instead of the story.

Display the transparency of Summer Days: Graph 2 (T80).

Now let's look at Graph 2. What do you notice about the graph? Don't say yet which day you think it is. Can you use any terms from the "Graphing Words" chart to describe how the temperature is changing?

Students may talk about its lopsided shape, that it starts to go down at noon, or that it is higher in the morning than the evening. As they comment about the shape of the graph, ask what it means in terms of what the temperatures were like.

If you were starting with the graph, what type of day do you think it would describe? What are some of the things that may have happened? Which story matches Graph 2? (*Friday's story*)

If time allows, discuss Saturday's story and display the transparency of Summer Days: Graph 1 (T79).

ACTIVITY

③ Winter Days

20 MIN PAIRS

Students work in pairs on *Student Activity Book* pages 19–20 to create their own stories about winter days to match each graph.

To introduce this activity, you may wish to make a list with your class of some outdoor activities and clothing appropriate for winter. Students may suggest the following:

Activities	Clothing
Ice skating	Hat
Sledding	Gloves
Building a snowman	Scarf
Taking a walk	Boots

Students will have time in the next session to continue their work on this sheet.

ONGOING ASSESSMENT: Observing Students at Work ✓

Students write stories to match the temperature changes shown on a graph.

- **Are students able to identify qualitative descriptions (hot, cool) with approximate temperatures?**

- **Can students interpret the trends in the temperature change shown on the graphs to inform their stories?**

SESSION FOLLOW-UP

④ Daily Practice and Homework

 Daily Practice: For ongoing review, have students complete *Student Activity Book* page 21.

 Homework: Students answer questions about two temperature graphs on *Student Activity Book* pages 23–24.

 Student Math Handbook: Students and families may use *Student Math Handbook* pages 66–69, 70, 71–72 for reference and review. See pages 156–161 in the back of this unit.

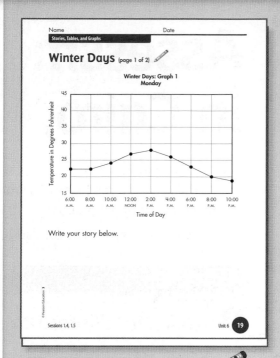

▲ Student Activity Book, pp. 19–20

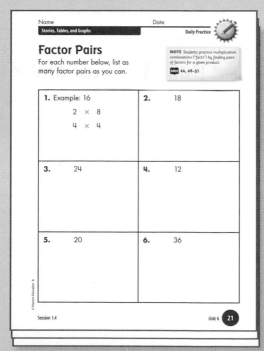

▲ Student Activity Book, pp. 21, 23–24

Assessment: A Summer Day in Cairo, Egypt

Math Focus Points

◆ Describing the overall shape of a line graph—increasing, decreasing, staying the same

◆ Associating a story with its corresponding graph

Today's Plan	Materials
ACTIVITY ❶ **Stories for Winter Days** 30 MIN PAIRS CLASS	• *Student Activity Book,* pp. 13, 19–20 (from Sessions 1.3 and 1.4) • T82–T83
ASSESSMENT ACTIVITY ❷ **A Summer Day in Cairo, Egypt** 30 MIN INDIVIDUALS	• M20–M21*
SESSION FOLLOW-UP ❸ **Daily Practice and Homework**	• *Student Activity Book,* pp. 25–26 • *Student Math Handbook,* pp. 70, 71–72

*See *Materials to Prepare,* p. 23.

ACTIVITY

Stories for Winter Days

30 MIN   PAIRS   CLASS

Students continue to work on *Student Activity Book* pages 19–20. As they finish, they read each other their stories while their partner follows along on each graph.

Students who finish their stories can complete any work remaining on *Student Activity Book* page 13 and write descriptions of how the temperature is changing on each part of the graph.

Students share stories that correspond to graphs.

When most students have something written for both stories, gather as a whole group and ask a few students to share their stories.

As [Kim] tells her story, I want all of you to think about which graph she is describing.

As students share stories and guess the corresponding graph, ask them what in the stories alerted them to the appropriate graph.

You may choose to display the corresponding transparency of Winter Days: Graphs 1 and 2 (T82–T83).

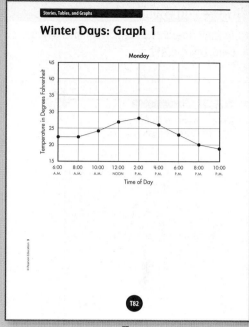

▲ Transparencies, T82

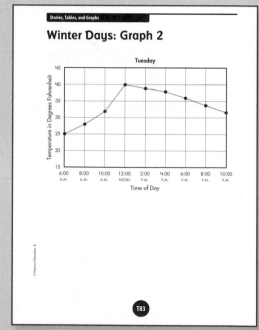

▲ Transparencies, T83

Professional Development

❶ Teacher Note: Assessment: A Summer Day in Cairo, Egypt, p. 119

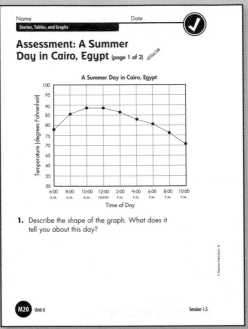

▲ Resource Masters, M20

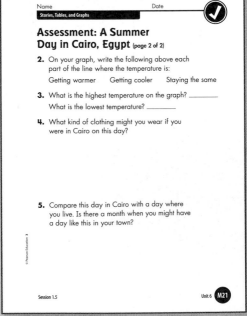

▲ Resource Master M21

ONGOING ASSESSMENT: Observing Students at Work

Students complete stories to match temperature graphs and consider what elements in the stories correspond to features of the graphs.

- **Are students able to identify qualitative descriptions (warm, cool) with approximate temperatures?**

- **Do students use features of the stories to identify the shape of the corresponding graph?**

ASSESSMENT ACTIVITY

② A Summer Day in Cairo, Egypt

30 MIN   INDIVIDUALS

Distribute copies of Assessment: A Summer Day in Cairo, Egypt (M20–M21). Students work individually to interpret a graph of the temperatures on a summer day in Cairo, Egypt. They describe the shape of the graph and explain what it shows about the temperature during that day. They also determine the highest and the lowest temperatures and what clothing might be worn on that day.❶

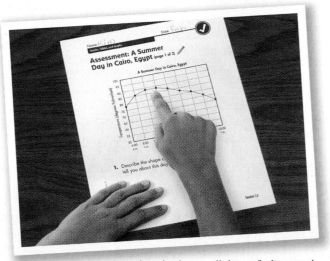

Students describe the overall shape of a line graph.

This assessment focuses on two of this unit's benchmarks. Problems 1–3 assess Benchmark 1: Interpret graphs of change over time, including both the meaning of points on a graph and how the graph shows that values are increasing and decreasing, or staying the same. Problems 4–5 assess Benchmark 2: Interpret temperature values (i.e., relate temperatures to seasons, to what outdoor clothing would be needed, and so on).

ONGOING ASSESSMENT: Observing Students at Work

Students answer questions about the overall trend in the graph and about changes in temperature.

- **Can students describe how the temperature is changing for parts of the day and for the day as a whole?**

- **Can students determine the highest and lowest temperatures from the graph?**

- **Can students relate the temperature values shown on the graph to people's experience of temperatures in the 70s and 80s?**

Make sure that students write complete answers, especially for Problem 1. They should describe how the temperature changes across the whole time period shown on the graph. For Problem 2, make sure that students understand that they are to write these phrases in appropriate places along the line graph.

SESSION FOLLOW-UP
Daily Practice and Homework

 Daily Practice: For ongoing review, have students complete *Student Activity Book* page 25.

 Homework: Students practice multiplication combinations ("facts") in related sets on *Student Activity Book* page 26.

 **Student Math Handbook:** Students and families may use *Student Math Handbook* pages 70, 71–72 for reference and review. See pages 156–161 in the back of this unit.

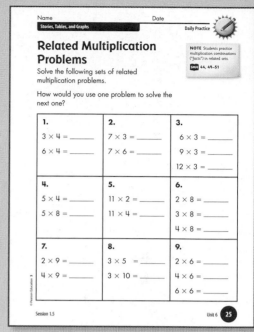

▲ **Student Activity Book, p. 25**

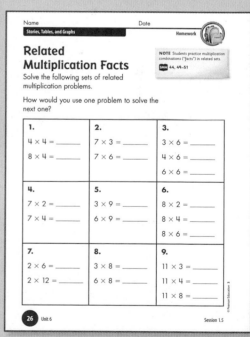

▲ **Student Activity Book, p. 26**

Mathematical Emphasis

Number Sequences Constructing, describing, and extending number sequences with constant increments generated by various contexts

Math Focus Points

◆ Identifying the unit of a repeating pattern

◆ Associating counting numbers with elements of a pattern

◆ Determining the element of an ABC pattern associated with a particular counting number

◆ Describing and extending a number sequence with a constant increment (e.g., 3, 6, 9, . . . or 2, 5, 8, . . .)

◆ Identifying numbers that are multiples of three, or one less or one more than a multiple of three

Cube Train Patterns

SESSION 2.1 p. 56	Student Activity Book	Student Math Handbook	Professional Development: Read Ahead of Time
Cube Patterns: Red, Blue, Green Students describe a red-blue-green repeating pattern and identify its unit. They determine what colors are associated with particular numbers when the cube pattern is numbered with the counting numbers.	27–29	73–74	• **Part 4: Ten-Minute Math and Classroom Routines** in *Implementing Investigations in Grade 3:* Today's Number • **Teacher Note:** Repeating Patterns and Counting Numbers, p. 124
SESSION 2.2 p. 62			
Where Are the Greens? Students describe the number sequence associated with the green cubes in the red-blue-green repeating pattern (3, 6, 9, 12, . . .) and consider why this number pattern occurs. They determine the number sequences for the red and blue cubes.	31–37	73–74	• **Dialogue Box:** Where Are the Greens? Blues? Reds?, p. 147
SESSION 2.3 p. 67			
What Color Is It? Students compare the three number sequences for each color in the red-blue-green repeating pattern. They use what they know about multiples of 3 to determine the color of cubes associated with particular numbers.	32–36, 38–41	73–74	

Materials to Gather	Materials to Prepare
• **Connecting cubes** (enough red, blue, and green for each student to have 4 of each color, plus extras) • **Hundred charts** (available in the classroom) • **Number lines** (available in the classroom)	• **Twelve-cube train in a red-blue-green repeating pattern** Prepare a train of 12 connecting cubes (red-blue-green-red-blue-green . . .) for use in the opening discussion.
• **Connecting cubes** (enough red, blue, and green for each student to have 4 of each color, plus extras) • **Twelve-cube train** (from Session 2.1)	
• **Connecting cubes** (enough red, blue, and green for each student to have 4 of each color, plus extras) • **Number lines** (available in the classroom)	

Cube Patterns: Red, Blue, Green

Math Focus Points

◆ Identifying the unit of a repeating pattern

◆ Associating counting numbers with elements of a pattern

◆ Determining the element of an ABC pattern associated with a particular counting number

Vocabulary

repeating pattern
unit

Today's Plan

		Materials
① DISCUSSION **Numbering Repeating Patterns** — 15 MIN CLASS		• 12-Cube Train*
② ACTIVITY **Cube Patterns** — 25 MIN INDIVIDUALS PAIRS		• *Student Activity Book,* p. 27 • Connecting cubes; hundred charts; number lines
③ DISCUSSION **The 25th Cube** — 20 MIN CLASS		
④ SESSION FOLLOW-UP **Daily Practice and Homework**		• *Student Activity Book,* pp. 28–29 • *Student Math Handbook,* pp. 73–74

*See *Materials to Prepare,* p. 55.

Ten-Minute Math

Today's Number Write the following expressions that equal 50 on the board and have students solve them:

$$(6 \times 6) + (6 \times 4) - 10 \qquad (5 \times 20) - (5 \times 10)$$
$$(100 \div 4) + (50 \div 2) \qquad (5 \times 5) \times 2$$

For each expression, ask students these questions:

• Which operations appear in the expression?

• How many operations are in the expression?

• How did you solve the problem?

If time remains, ask students to create their own expressions that equal 50.

DISCUSSION
Numbering Repeating Patterns

15 MIN   CLASS

Professional Development

❶ **Teacher Note:** Repeating Patterns and Counting Numbers, p. 124

Math Focus Points for Discussion

◆ Identifying the unit of a repeating pattern

◆ Associating counting numbers with elements of a pattern

In this discussion, students review ideas from Grade 2 about how repeating patterns are constructed by iterating a unit (the part of the pattern that repeats). They are introduced to the idea of applying numbers to a repeating pattern of colored cubes.❶

Introduce this Investigation briefly.

Some of you may remember when you worked with color patterns, using the connecting cubes in Grade 2. We're going to work for a few days on repeating patterns. By numbering the cubes, we'll be able to use the numbers to describe how a repeating pattern changes. We'll also figure out what color certain cubes will be—such as the 50th cube or the 100th cube—without actually building the pattern all the way to 50 or 100 cubes.

Show students the 12-cube train you prepared with the pattern: red-blue-green, red-blue-green, red-blue-green, red-blue-green.

This is a repeating pattern. What do you see in this pattern? How would you describe it?

Use students' language and observations to bring out the idea that the unit for this pattern is three cubes long and is *red-blue-green*. If students worked with the Grade 2 Patterns and Functions unit last year, you can refer to that experience.

Last year when you worked on patterns, you talked about the unit of a repeating pattern. What is the unit of this pattern? How many cubes are there in the part that repeats over and over?

Ask students whether they can come up with other patterns, using numbers or letters or body movements that have the same kind of pattern as this color pattern. For example, sometimes students suggest "1-2-3, 1-2-3" or "a-b-c, a-b-c" or come up with a body movement pattern such as slap knees-clap-tap shoulders. It is helpful to show how the red-blue-green pattern matches these other patterns by having the class chant "red,

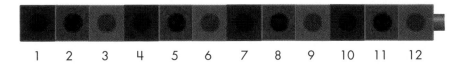

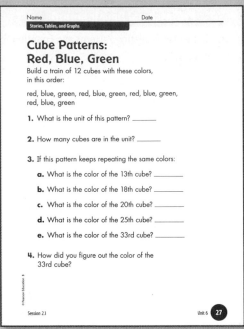

Name _____ Date _____

Stories, Tables, and Graphs

**Cube Patterns:
Red, Blue, Green**

Build a train of 12 cubes with these colors,
in this order:

red, blue, green, red, blue, green, red, blue, green,
red, blue, green

1. What is the unit of this pattern? _____

2. How many cubes are in the unit? _____

3. If this pattern keeps repeating the same colors:

   a. What is the color of the 13th cube? _____

   b. What is the color of the 18th cube? _____

   c. What is the color of the 20th cube? _____

   d. What is the color of the 25th cube? _____

   e. What is the color of the 33rd cube? _____

4. How did you figure out the color of the
   33rd cube?

Session 2.1   Unit 6 **27**

▲ **Student Activity Book, p. 27**

blue, green" along with the body movements or point to the colors in turn as you say "1, 2, 3." Students also worked on these kinds of correspondences in Grade 2.

Now introduce the idea of associating the counting numbers with the cubes.

1 2 3 4 5 6 7 8 9 10 11 12

The first cube is red. What color is the second cube? What color is the sixth cube? What color is the eighth cube? Now I want you to imagine that this pattern keeps going on past the cubes I am holding. What color would the next cube be? What number would that be? What color would the 15th cube be? How do you know?

Keep this discussion brief because students need time to work on these ideas in the next activity.

ACTIVITY

2 Cube Patterns

25 MIN INDIVIDUALS PAIRS

Students build a train of twelve cubes with the same red-blue-green pattern. Using their cube trains as a tool, they answer the questions on *Student Activity Book* page 27. In these questions, students determine the colors associated with particular numbers when the cubes are labeled with the counting numbers, starting at one.

Students should begin by working individually and then, after about 10 to 15 minutes, share their thinking with a partner, both to check whether they have the same answers and to explain their methods. Let students know that they will be sharing methods at the end of class and that this is a good time to practice explaining how they determined the colors of certain cubes.

Students use the unit of a repeating pattern to extend the pattern.

ONGOING ASSESSMENT: Observing Students at Work

Students find which elements of a repeating red-blue-green pattern correspond to particular counting numbers (e.g., the 18th element, the 25th element).

- **Are students able to determine the element of the pattern associated with a particular counting number?**
  For example:

  the 13th cube (red)

  the 18th cube (green)

  the 20th cube (blue)

  the 25th cube (red)

  the 33rd cube (green)

- **How do students determine the color of a particular element?**
  Do they build the pattern up to that point? Do they use multiples of three to help them?

Students should use whatever tools they find useful, including number lines or 100 charts. Some students realize even at this early part of the Investigation that the green cubes always fall on multiples of three. They then use a 100 chart to identify the multiples of three to support their thinking.

DIFFERENTIATION: Supporting the Range of Learners

Intervention For some students, building on more cubes may help them understand the red-blue-green pattern. However, many third graders can begin to reason about the pattern without building more of it. Use your judgment about discouraging some students from building on more cubes and then counting by ones.

- You figured out the color of the 18th cube by building on more cubes up to 18. Do you think you can figure out a way to solve the next problem without building on more cubes?

ELL Students who did not participate in the Grade 2 *Investigations* curriculum might need extra support in order to understand cube train patterns and related vocabulary, such as *repeating pattern* and *unit*. English Language Learners may also need the vocabulary support to understand these key terms. You can preview this information in a small group before starting this Investigation, or reinforce key vocabulary and concepts as necessary during each session.

3 DISCUSSION

20 MIN CLASS

The 25th Cube

Math Focus Points for Discussion

◆ Associating counting numbers with elements of a pattern

◆ Determining the element of an ABC pattern associated with a particular counting number

Begin the discussion by asking students how they figured out the color for the 18th cube.

Students may have noticed that to get 18 cubes, they must add on two more units of the pattern (red-blue-green, red-blue-green) to their 12-cube train, landing on green for 18 as they did for 12.

Why do you think the 12th cube and the 18th cube are both green?

You can get out some initial ideas here, but keep in mind that students will work more on what numbers are associated with the green cubes during Session 2.2.

Then ask students to share methods for finding the color of the 25th cube (red). If all students agree that it is red, ask them to share their methods for figuring that out. If students disagree, ask them to share their methods to see whether they can convince their classmates.

Students might say:

 "Oscar and I put our cubes together and we got 24. So the 25th is a red because it starts the pattern all over again."

 "24 is green because it is two 12s put together. If you add one, red comes after green, so it is red."

 "I had my 100 chart and I went by three. So every shaded part on the 100 chart is green. And a red plus two more is a green. 27 is a multiple of three and it's green. It's two more than red, so the 25th is red."

SESSION FOLLOW-UP
4 Daily Practice and Homework

 Daily Practice: For ongoing review, have students complete *Student Activity Book* page 28.

 Homework: Students solve multiplication problems on *Student Activity Book* page 29.

 Student Math Handbook: Students and families may use *Student Math Handbook* pages 73–74 for reference and review. See pages 156–161 in the back of this unit.

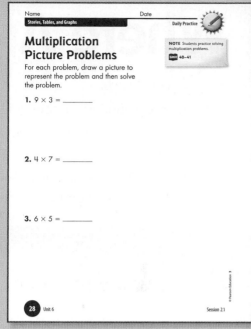

Name _____ Date _____
Stories, Tables, and Graphs   Daily Practice

Multiplication Picture Problems

NOTE Students practice solving multiplication problems.
SMH 40–41

For each problem, draw a picture to represent the problem and then solve the problem.

1. $9 \times 3 =$ _____

2. $4 \times 7 =$ _____

3. $6 \times 5 =$ _____

28 Unit 6   Session 2.1

▲ **Student Activity Book, p. 28**

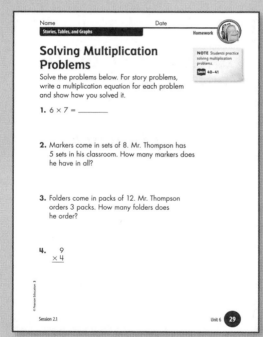

Name _____ Date _____
Stories, Tables, and Graphs   Homework

Solving Multiplication Problems

NOTE Students practice solving multiplication problems.
SMH 40–41

Solve the problems below. For story problems, write a multiplication equation for each problem and show how you solved it.

1. $6 \times 7 =$ _____

2. Markers come in sets of 8. Mr. Thompson has 5 sets in his classroom. How many markers does he have in all?

3. Folders come in packs of 12. Mr. Thompson orders 3 packs. How many folders does he order?

4. $\begin{array}{r} 9 \\ \times 4 \\ \hline \end{array}$

Session 2.1   Unit 6 29

▲ **Student Activity Book, p. 29**

Where Are the Greens?

Math Focus Points

◆ Associating counting numbers with elements of a pattern

◆ Describing and extending a number sequence with a constant increment (e.g., 3, 6, 9, . . . or 2, 5, 8, . . .)

◆ Determining the element of an ABC pattern associated with a particular counting number

Vocabulary

multiple

Today's Plan		Materials
ACTIVITY ❶ **Examining the Green Cubes**	🕐 20 MIN 👤 INDIVIDUALS 👥 PAIRS	• *Student Activity Book*, pp. 31–32 • 12-Cube Trains (from Session 2.1)
DISCUSSION ❷ **Where Are the Greens?**	🕐 20 MIN 👥 CLASS	• *Student Activity Book*, p. 32 • Connecting cubes
ACTIVITY ❸ **Examining the Red and Blue Cubes**	🕐 20 MIN 👤 INDIVIDUALS 👥 PAIRS	• *Student Activity Book*, pp. 33–36 • Connecting cubes
SESSION FOLLOW-UP ❹ **Daily Practice**		• *Student Activity Book*, p. 37 • *Student Math Handbook*, pp. 73–74

Ten-Minute Math

Today's Number Students create expressions that equal 49. They can use any combination of the four operations but must use at least two operations in each expression they create.

$$(7 \times 7) + 10 - 10 = 49 \qquad (100 \div 2) + 10 - 11 = 49$$

Collect a few expressions to write on the board. Ask students to explain which part of the expression they solved first and how they know that the expression equals 49.

ACTIVITY

1 Examining the Green Cubes

20 MIN INDIVIDUALS PAIRS

Introduce this activity briefly by holding up the red-blue-green 12-cube train.

If we count these cubes 1, 2, 3, 4 and so on, as we did in the last class, what number is matched with the first green cube? What about the second green cube? You're going to work on the numbers that match up with the green cubes if this pattern keeps going.

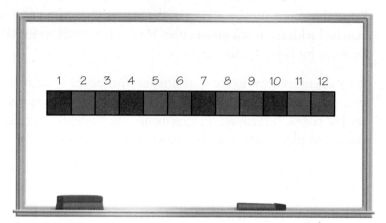

Students work individually or in pairs on *Student Activity Book* pages 31–32.

✔ ONGOING ASSESSMENT: Observing Students at Work

Students find the numbers associated with the green cubes in the red-blue-green pattern: multiples of 3.

- **Do students find the number sequence 3, 6, 9, . . . that is associated with the third element in the pattern (the green cubes)?**

- **Do students notice the relationship between the number sequence and the length of the unit of the pattern?**

As you observe students working, make sure that they understand the difference between finding the number associated with the first cube in the pattern and the number associated with the first *green* cube in the pattern.

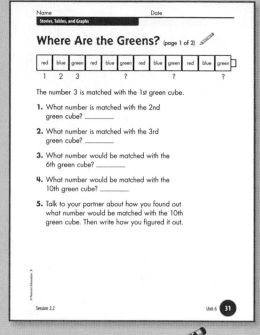

Where Are the Greens? (page 1 of 2)

| red | blue | green | red | blue | green | red | blue | green | red | blue | green |
| 1 | 2 | 3 | | | ? | | | ? | | | ? |

The number 3 is matched with the 1st green cube.

1. What number is matched with the 2nd green cube? _____

2. What number is matched with the 3rd green cube? _____

3. What number would be matched with the 6th green cube? _____

4. What number would be matched with the 10th green cube? _____

5. Talk to your partner about how you found out what number would be matched with the 10th green cube. Then write how you figured it out.

Session 2.2   Unit 6   **31**

▲ **Student Activity Book, p. 31** WRITING

Where Are the Greens? (page 2 of 2)

6. What are the numbers for the first 10 green cubes?

1st green _____   6th green _____

2nd green _____   7th green _____

3rd green _____   8th green _____

4th green _____   9th green _____

5th green _____   10th green _____

7. What are you noticing about the numbers that are matched with the green cubes? Why does it work that way?

32 Unit 6   Sessions 2.2, 2.3

▲ **Student Activity Book, p. 32** WRITING

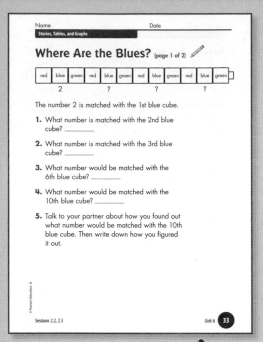

Name _____ Date _____
Stories, Tables, and Graphs

Where Are the Blues? (page 1 of 2)

red	blue	green	red	blue	green	red	blue	green	red	blue	green	
2		?		?			?					

The number 2 is matched with the 1st blue cube.

1. What number is matched with the 2nd blue cube? _____

2. What number is matched with the 3rd blue cube? _____

3. What number would be matched with the 6th blue cube? _____

4. What number would be matched with the 10th blue cube? _____

5. Talk to your partner about how you found out what number would be matched with the 10th blue cube. Then write down how you figured it out.

Sessions 2.2, 2.3   Unit 6 **33**

▲ **Student Activity Book, p. 33**

Name _____ Date _____
Stories, Tables, and Graphs

Where Are the Blues? (page 2 of 2)

6. What are the numbers for the first 10 blue cubes?

1st blue _____   6th blue _____

2nd blue _____   7th blue _____

3rd blue _____   8th blue _____

4th blue _____   9th blue _____

5th blue _____   10th blue _____

7. What are you noticing about the numbers that are matched with the blue cubes? Why does it work that way?

8. The 13th blue cube in the pattern matches with 38. What number matches with the 14th blue cube? _____

How do you know?

34 Unit 6   Sessions 2.2, 2.3

▲ **Student Activity Book, p. 34**

20 MIN   CLASS

DISCUSSION

② Where Are the Greens?

Math Focus Points for Discussion

◆ Describing and extending a number sequence with a constant increment (e.g., 3, 6, 9, . . . or 2, 5, 8 . . .)

◆ Determining the element of an ABC pattern associated with a particular counting number

Begin this discussion by asking students to explain what number is matched with the tenth green cube. Have a few students explain their methods for finding this number.

Ask pairs of students to compare answers for the list of numbers associated with the first ten green cubes. Have a student write the sequence on the easel or board. If there are disagreements, ask students to explain to one another until they agree on the sequence of 3, 6, 9, 12 . . . 30.

After the numbers for the first ten green cubes have been written down, ask students about this sequence.

What do you know about these numbers?

Students might say:

"These are the counting by 3 numbers" or "You skip two numbers each time."

You can use this as an opportunity to introduce the term multiple. Then ask for responses to Problem 7 on *Student Activity Book* page 32.

Why does it work this way? Why do you think the numbers for the green cubes are multiples of three?

This question provides an opportunity for students to talk about how the length of the unit of the pattern is related to the number sequence.

Students might say:

"You skip the red and blue, and green is always the third one. It's just like skip counting by 3s."

"Green is the last one and there are three cubes, so green is number three. So when you count by three, you're always going to land on green."

Note that these ideas will be continued in the activities and discussion in the next session. In this discussion, students can start thinking and talking about their ideas. However, they should have time to go on to the next activity, which will give them more experience with the number sequences that are matched with this pattern. **❶**

ACTIVITY

③ Examining the Red and Blue Cubes

20 MIN INDIVIDUALS PAIRS

Tell students that they will now find the number sequences for the blue and red cubes.

As you work on the next questions, think about what you know about the green cubes to help you with the blue and red cubes.

Students work individually or in pairs on *Student Activity Book* pages 33–36. Students will have time to continue working on these pages in the next session.

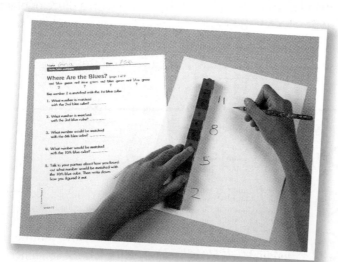

Students use connecting cubes to associate counting numbers with elements of a pattern.

Professional Development

❶ Dialogue Box: Where Are the Greens? Blues? Reds?, p. 147

Name _____ Date _____

Stories, Tables, and Graphs

Where Are the Reds? (page 1 of 2)

red	blue	green	red	blue	green	red	blue	green	red	blue	green
1			?			?			?		

The number 1 is matched with the 1st red cube.

1. What number is matched with the 2nd red cube? _____

2. What number is matched with the 3rd red cube? _____

3. What number would be matched with the 6th red cube? _____

4. What number would be matched with the 10th red cube? _____

5. Talk to your partner about how you found out what number would be matched with the 10th red cube. Then write down how you figured it out.

Sessions 2.2, 2.3   Unit 6   **35**

▲ **Student Activity Book, p. 35** WRITING

Name _____ Date _____

Stories, Tables, and Graphs

Where Are the Reds? (page 2 of 2)

6. What are the numbers for the first 10 red cubes?

1st red _____	6th red _____
2nd red _____	7th red _____
3rd red _____	8th red _____
4th red _____	9th red _____
5th red _____	10th red _____

7. What are you noticing about the numbers that are matched with the red cubes? Why does it work that way?

8. The 12th red cube in the pattern matches with 34. What number matches with the 13th red cube? _____

How do you know?

36 Unit 6   Sessions 2.2, 2.3

▲ **Student Activity Book, p. 36** WRITING

Name _____ Date _____

Stories, Tables, and Graphs

Daily Practice

**Things That
Come in Groups**

Solve the story problems below. Write a
multiplication equation for each problem
and show how you solved it.

NOTE Students practice multiplication by solving story problems.

SMH 40–41

Spiders have 8 legs.

1. How many legs do 3 spiders have? _____

Equation: _3 × 8 =_ _____

2. How many legs do 4 spiders have? _____

Equation: _____

3. How many legs do 5 spiders have? _____

Equation: _____

Session 2.2

Unit 6 **37**

▲ **Student Activity Book, p. 37**

ONGOING ASSESSMENT: Observing Students at Work

Students find the number sequences associated with the blue and red cubes in the red-blue-green pattern.

- **Do students determine 2, 5, 8, 11, 14, . . . as the sequence for the blue cubes?**

- **Do students determine 1, 4, 7, 10, 13, . . . as the sequence for the red cubes?**

- **Do students notice that any two consecutive cubes of the same color are three apart in the number sequence?**

- **Do students use the numbers for the green cubes to find the numbers for the blue or red cubes (e.g., the number of the sixth blue cube is one less than the number of the sixth green cube)?**

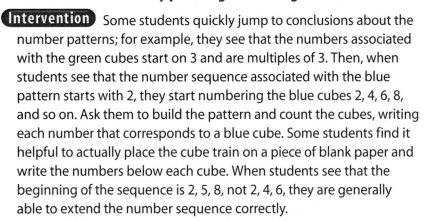

DIFFERENTIATION: Supporting the Range of Learners

Intervention Some students quickly jump to conclusions about the number patterns; for example, they see that the numbers associated with the green cubes start on 3 and are multiples of 3. Then, when students see that the number sequence associated with the blue pattern starts with 2, they start numbering the blue cubes 2, 4, 6, 8, and so on. Ask them to build the pattern and count the cubes, writing each number that corresponds to a blue cube. Some students find it helpful to actually place the cube train on a piece of blank paper and write the numbers below each cube. When students see that the beginning of the sequence is 2, 5, 8, not 2, 4, 6, they are generally able to extend the number sequence correctly.

SESSION FOLLOW-UP
4 Daily Practice

Daily Practice: For ongoing review, have students complete *Student Activity Book* page 37.

Student Math Handbook: Students and families may use *Student Math Handbook* pages 73–74 for reference and review. See pages 156–161 in the back of this unit.

What Color Is It?

Math Focus Points

◆ Describing and extending a number sequence with a constant increment (e.g., 3, 6, 9, . . . or 2, 5, 8, . . .)

◆ Determining the element of an ABC pattern associated with a particular counting number

◆ Identifying numbers that are multiples of 3, or 1 less or 1 more than a multiple of 3

Today's Plan		Materials
ACTIVITY ❶ **Examining the Red and Blue Cubes**	15 MIN INDIVIDUALS PAIRS	• *Student Activity Book,* pp. 33–36 (from Session 2.2) • Connecting cubes
ACTIVITY ❷ **What Color Is It?**	15 MIN INDIVIDUALS PAIRS	• *Student Activity Book,* pp. 32 (from Session 2.2), 38–39
DISCUSSION ❸ **Three Apart Sequences**	30 MIN CLASS	• *Student Activity Book,* pp. 32, 34, 36 • Number lines
SESSION FOLLOW-UP ❹ **Daily Practice and Homework**		• *Student Activity Book,* pp. 40–41 • *Student Math Handbook,* pp. 73–74

Ten-Minute Math

Today's Number Students create expressions that equal 500. They must use addition and multiplication combinations that equal 100 in each expression they create. For example: $(72 + 28) + (4 \times 25) + (50 \times 2) + (37 + 63) + 100 = 500$. Collect a few expressions to write on the board and ask students these questions:

• Which numbers in your expression equal 100?

• How can you make sure that this expression equals 500?

Professional Development

❶ **Teacher Note:** Repeating Patterns and Counting Numbers, p. 124

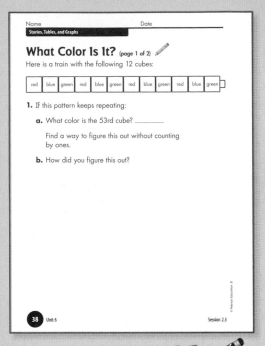

Name _____ Date _____

Stories, Tables, and Graphs

What Color Is It? (page 1 of 2)

Here is a train with the following 12 cubes:

| red | blue | green | red | blue | green | red | blue | green | red | blue | green | |

1. If this pattern keeps repeating:

    a. What color is the 53rd cube? _____

    Find a way to figure this out without counting by ones.

    b. How did you figure this out?

38 Unit 6   Session 2.3

▲ **Student Activity Book, p. 38**  WRITING

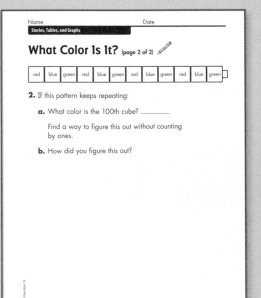

Name _____ Date _____

Stories, Tables, and Graphs

What Color Is It? (page 2 of 2)

| red | blue | green | red | blue | green | red | blue | green | red | blue | green | |

2. If this pattern keeps repeating:

    a. What color is the 100th cube? _____

    Find a way to figure this out without counting by ones.

    b. How did you figure this out?

Session 2.3   Unit 6 39

▲ **Student Activity Book, p. 39** WRITING

ACTIVITY

1 Examining the Red and Blue Cubes

15 MIN INDIVIDUALS PAIRS

Students complete their work on their own or in pairs on *Student Activity Book* pages 33–36. For complete details about this activity, see Session 2.2, page 65.

ONGOING ASSESSMENT: Observing Students at Work

Students find the number sequences associated with the blue cubes and with the red cubes in the red-blue-green pattern.

● **Do students determine 2, 5, 8, 11, 14, . . . as the sequence for the blue cubes?**

● **Do students determine 1, 4, 7, 10, 13, . . . as the sequence for the red cubes?**

● **Do the students notice that any two consecutive cubes of the same color are three apart?**

● **Do students use the numbers for the green cubes to find the numbers for the blue or red cubes (e.g., the number of the sixth blue cube is one less than the number of the sixth green cube)?**

ACTIVITY

2 What Color Is It?

15 MIN INDIVIDUALS PAIRS

As students complete their work on *Student Activity Book* pages 33–36, they can begin working on *Student Activity Book* pages 38–39. On these two pages, students find the color of the 53rd cube (*blue*) and the 100th cube (*red*) and explain how they figured out the colors of these cubes.❶

ONGOING ASSESSMENT: Observing Students at Work

Students use what they know about the number sequences associated with the red-blue-green repeating pattern to determine the color of cubes associated with particular numbers.

- **Can students find the color of a certain cube without counting or making the pattern all the way up to that number cube?**

- **Do students recognize that all green cubes are associated with multiples of 3?**

- **Do students use the number sequence for the green cubes to help determine the color of a cube matched with a certain number (e.g., 100 is 1 more than 99; 99 is a multiple of 3 and must be green, so the 100th cube is red)?**

Sometimes students just write the color of the cube and an arithmetic expression in response to the questions. For example, a student might write "blue" and "9 × 6" for the question about the 53rd cube. Ask students to elaborate on their answer to make it clear how they are using 9 × 6 to solve the problem.

DIFFERENTIATION: Supporting the Range of Learners

Intervention As you talk with students while they work, help students find strategies that do not require counting up by ones or building the cube train up to that point. For example, you may ask students, "Do you know a number that would match a green cube that is close to 53?" Students can look at their list of numbers for green cubes on *Student Activity Book* page 32. If the problems on *Student Activity Book* pages 38–39 are too difficult for some students, you can choose other numbers for particular students. Choose a smaller number that is one more than a multiple of three (which will be associated with the red cube) and another smaller number that is one less than a multiple of three (which will be associated with the blue cube).

Extension If the problems on *Student Activity Book* pages 38–39 are not challenging enough for some students, you can choose other numbers for particular students. Choose a larger number that is one more than a multiple of three (which will be associated with the red cube) and another larger number that is one less than a multiple of three (which will be associated with the blue cube).

Professional Development

❷ **Dialogue Box:** Where Are the Greens? Blues? Reds?, p. 147

DISCUSSION

③ Three Apart Sequences

30 MIN   CLASS

Math Focus Points for Discussion

◆ Determining the element of an ABC pattern associated with a particular counting number

◆ Identifying numbers that are multiples of three, or one less or more than a multiple of three

Have one student write the list of numbers for the greens from *Student Activity Book* page 32; another student for the blues from *Student Activity Book* page 34; another student for the reds from *Student Activity Book* page 36. Have the numbers in a list under the words Red, Blue, Green.

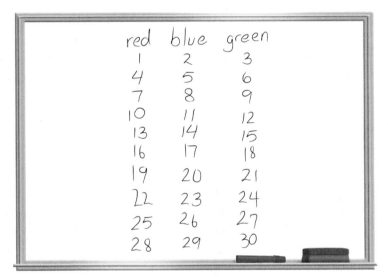

Do all of you agree that these are the right numbers?

If there is any disagreement, the class should talk about it until everyone agrees. Ask students what they notice about the three number sequences.

We talked about the list of numbers for the green cubes the other day. What do you notice about the list of numbers for the blue cubes? What about for the red cubes? What else do you notice?

Some students may say that on each list, the numbers are three apart. Others may notice that every number from 1 to 30 is on some list. Still others may see that the numbers in the sequence for the red cubes are each two less than the numbers for the sequence for the green cubes or that the numbers in the sequence for the blue cubes are each one less than the numbers for the sequence for the green cubes.❷

Students might say:

"You can count by 3 anywhere. It's the same for blue. You go to that color and you add 3 and you still hit it."

"I noticed when I did blue that the number went down one—2, 5, 8—it's one number behind green."

"You land on different numbers if you add on 3. For 3s you land on 6 for your second number and for blues you land on 5 and for reds you land on 4."

When students describe each sequence as being three apart, some teachers find it useful to show the green number sequence on a number line, then the blue and red sequences on parallel number lines.

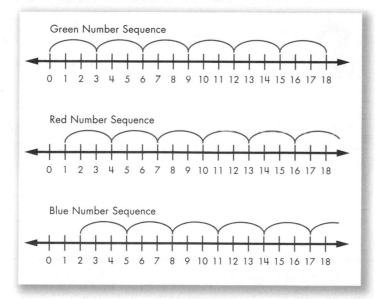

Then ask about how students would find the color for a particular number cube. Start with a multiple of three higher than 30 but lower than 52, such as 42 or 45.

Can you figure out which sequence the number 45 would be in?

Give students a few minutes to talk to a neighbor about this and then solicit some responses. When it is established that 45 will be in the sequence of green, ask about 46 and 44.

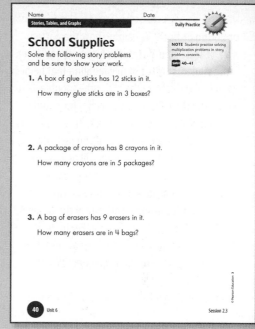

▲ **Student Activity Book, p. 40**

Math Note

❸ **Doubling or Not?** Visualizing how the pattern works can become difficult as numbers get larger. Some students try to use the doubling that helped them find the color of the 25th cube (double 12 to get 24 and then it is one more cube) for numbers for which doubling does not work. Kim knows that the 25th cube is red and says, "If you just add another 25 and get 50, it would still be red. So then count on 3 more cubes, and the 53rd is red." Why this doubling idea works in some cases and not in others is considered directly in the Grade 4 unit Penny Jars and Plant Growth. For now, if students are using a doubling strategy that does not work, they may need to build two 25-cube trains and actually try to put them together in order to see that they cannot attach the ending red cube of one to the beginning red cube of the other without breaking the red-blue-green pattern.

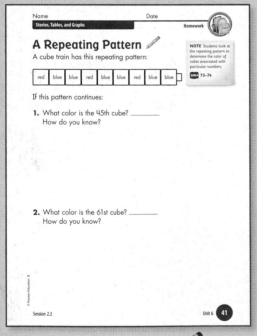

▲ **Student Activity Book, p. 41**

How can you use what you know about 45 to figure out what colors the 46th or 44th cubes are?

Solicit a few responses. Then ask about the colors that correspond to the numbers they worked on in the last activity: 53 (*blue*) and 100 (*red*).

Who had a way to find the color of the 53rd cube without counting by ones? Who has a different way? How did you find the color for the 100th cube?

Students might say:❸

 "I think it might be blue because 54 is green—it is a counting by 3 number—and you minus one, so it's blue."

 "I went up to 60, and I know that's green. It's a multiple of 3. So then I counted back. 3 back is 57—that's green—then 3 more, that's 54, so that's green. So then count back 1, and it's blue."

 "I did 12 and 12 and 12 and 12, that got me to 48. Then I counted up 5, and I got blue."

To finish the class, and this Investigation, ask students whether they have come up with any methods they can explain for determining the color of a certain number cube in the red-blue-green repeating pattern.

If I gave you a number, how would you go about figuring out whether that cube is red or blue or green?

SESSION FOLLOW-UP

4 Daily Practice and Homework

Daily Practice: For ongoing review, have students complete *Student Activity Book* page 40.

Homework: Students identify the color of cubes associated with particular numbers on *Activity Book* page 41.

Student Math Handbook: Students and families may use *Student Math Handbook* pages 73–74 for reference and review. See pages 156–161 in the back of this unit.

Mathematical Emphases

Using Tables and Graphs Using graphs to represent change

Math Focus Points

◆ Identifying points on a graph with corresponding values in a table and interpreting the numerical information in terms of the situation the graph represents

◆ Comparing situations by describing differences in their graphs

◆ Plotting points on a graph to represent a situation in which one quantity is changing in relation to another

Using Tables and Graphs Using tables to represent change

Math Focus Points

◆ Using tables to represent the relationship between two quantities in a situation with a constant rate of change

◆ Interpreting numbers in a table in terms of the situation they represent

◆ Comparing situations by describing differences in the tables that represent them

Linear Change Describing and representing constant change

Math Focus Points

◆ Describing the relationship between two quantities in a situation with a constant rate of change, taking into account a beginning amount and a constant increase

◆ Creating a representation for a situation with a constant rate of change

◆ Comparing different representations that show the same situation

◆ Making rules that relate one variable to the other in situations with a constant rate of change

◆ Connecting the steps of a general method or rule to the parts of the situation they represent

Representing a Constant Rate of Change

	Student Activity Book	Student Math Handbook	Professional Development: Read Ahead of Time	
SESSION 3.1 p. 78				
The Marbles of Rhomaar Students represent the story of a child who receives a certain number of marbles each night. They discuss how different representations show the starting amount, the constant rate of increase, and the ending amount.	43–47	75–80	• **Teacher Note:** Students' Representations of Change, p. 126	
SESSION 3.2 p. 85				
Working with Tables Students use a table to represent and compare two situations with a constant rate of change. They develop methods for determining the total number of marbles on every fifth day, leading to the articulation of a rule for any day.	49–52	81–86	• **Dialogue Box:** "He's Taking Bigger Steps, So He'll Catch Up", p. 149 • **Dialogue Box:** Why Are There Five 2s?, p. 151 • **Teacher Note:** Using and Interpreting Tables, p. 128	
SESSION 3.3 p. 92				
Describing a Rule Students complete tables to show several sequences of change and develop rules that describe the relationship between two variables (the number of days and the total number of marbles).	49, 53–57	87		
SESSION 3.4 p. 97				
Making Graphs from Tables Students develop rules for describing the relationship between two variables (number of days and total number of marbles). They use graphs to represent and compare two situations with different rates of change.	53–55, 59–64	75–80, 81–86, 87	• **Teacher Note:** Graphs of Situations with a Constant Rate of Change, p. 130	

Materials to Gather	Materials to Prepare
• **M22, Franick, Bolar, and Zupin** • **Colored pencils or crayons** (optional)	• **Chart Paper** Prepare the "Rhomaarian Children" class chart. On chart paper, show each child's name, the starting number of (or "leftover") marbles, and the nightly amount. Because the names are unfamiliar, students often forget the gender of each child, so you may want to include a sketch of each child's face. Keep in mind that you will be adding 5 other children's data in the course of the Investigation. See page 80 for an example. • **Sharing Student Representations** Decide how students will share their representations for the discussion at the end of the session (on overhead transparencies, on the board, and so on).
• **T84–T85, Table for Franick and Bolar** 🖨	• **Chart: "Rhomaarian Children" class chart** Add the data for Tovar to the class chart of data. (from Session 3.1) • **Table of Tovar's Marbles** Make a table that shows the beginning amount, Day 5, and Day 10 for Tovar, with only the beginning amount filled in. • **Chart paper** Copy the Table for Franick and Bolar (M23–M24) onto chart paper. Data for the first 7 days should be filled in. (optional)
• **Calculators** (1 per student; optional)	• **Chart: "Rhomaarian Children" class chart** Add the data for Winger and Jorad to the class chart of data. (from Session 3.1)
• **T86, Who Is It?** 🖨 • **Calculator** (optional) • **Chart: "Rhomaarian Children" class chart** (from Session 3.1) • **Colored pencils or crayons** (optional)	• **M26, Graphs for Tovar and Winger** Make copies. (as needed) • **Chart paper** Copy the transparency Who Is It?(T86) onto chart paper. (optional)

🖨 Overhead Transparency

Representing a Constant Rate of Change, *continued*

		Student Activity Book	Student Math Handbook	Professional Development: Read Ahead of Time	
SESSION 3.5 p. 103					
Using Graphs to Compare Students make and use graphs to represent and compare pairs of marble sequences, including sequences that start at the same point and then diverge and sequences that intersect.		53, 59–63, 65–69	75–80, 81–86		
SESSION 3.6 p. 108					
What Do the Graphs Show? Students continue making graphs to represent and compare pairs of marble sequences, including sequences that have different starting amounts but the same rate of change. They discuss what the graphs would look like if the change continued in the same way.		53, 61–63, 65–67, 71–72	75–80, 81–86	• **Dialogue Box:** Using Graphs to Compare Situations with a Constant Rate of Change, p. 153	
SESSION 3.7 p. 112					
End-of-Unit Assessment Students work on two problem sets as an end-of-unit assessment. One involves describing and comparing temperature graphs. The other focuses on using information in a table to describe and compare situations with constant rates of change.		73	66–69, 70, 75–80, 81–86	• **Teacher Note:** End-of-Unit Assessment, p. 134	

Materials to Gather	Materials to Prepare
• **T87, Completed Graphs for Tovar and Winger** 🖥 • **Colored pencils or crayons** (optional)	• **Chart: "Rhomaarian Children" class chart** Add the data for Gowen and Lazik to the class chart of data. (from Session 3.1) • **Chart paper** Copy the transparency Completed Graphs for Tovar and Winger (T87) onto chart paper. (optional)
• **T88, Completed Graphs for Tovar and Gowen** 🖥 • **T89, Completed Graphs for Tovar and Lazik** 🖥 • **Colored pencils or crayons** (optional)	• **Chart paper** Copy the transparency Completed Graphs for Tovar and Gowen (T88) onto chart paper. (optional) • **Chart paper** Copy the transparency Completed Graphs for Tovar and Lazik (T89) onto chart paper. (optional)
	• **M30–M36 End-of-Unit Assessment** Make copies. (1 per student)

🖥 Overhead Transparency

The Marbles of Rhomaar

Math Focus Points

◆ Describing the relationship between two quantities in a situation with a constant rate of change, taking into account a beginning amount and a constant increase

◆ Creating a representation for a situation with a constant rate of change

◆ Comparing different representations that show the same situation

Today's Plan		Materials
❶ ACTIVITY **The Magic Marbles of Rhomaar**	10 MIN CLASS	• Chart paper*
❷ ACTIVITY **Representing Marble Stories**	25 MIN PAIRS	• *Student Activity Book,* pp. 43–45 • Colored pencils or crayons (optional)
❸ DISCUSSION **Comparing Representations**	25 MIN CLASS	• *Student Activity Book,* pp. 43–45 • M22
❹ SESSION FOLLOW-UP **Daily Practice and Homework**		• *Student Activity Book,* pp. 46–47 • *Student Math Handbook,* pp. 75–80

*See *Materials to Prepare,* p. 75.

Ten-Minute Math

Today's Number Students create expressions that equal 163. They must use at least two multiples of 10 and at least two operations in each expression they create. For example: $200 - 50 + 20 - 7 = 163$ $(20 \times 5) + (20 \times 3) + 3 = 163$

Collect a few expressions to write on the board and ask students these questions:

· How did you decide to combine the numbers?

· How do you know that they equal 163?

ACTIVITY

① The Magic Marbles of Rhomaar

10 MIN   CLASS

Tell students the story of the Magic Marbles of Rhomaar, the context for their work on constructing representations of change in this investigation.

For the next several days, we will explore the growth patterns of Magic Marbles that children on the planet Rhomaar receive as gifts. The children on Rhomaar can use these Magic Marbles to buy toys, books, snacks, and any other things they like. For the first thirty nights of every year, each child on Rhomaar is visited by a Magic Marble Messenger, who leaves that child the same number of Magic Marbles each night. The odd thing, though, is that the number of Magic Marbles received by one child each night can be different from the number of Magic Marbles received by another child each night. So, different Rhomaarian children can get different numbers of Magic Marbles. No one on Rhomaar knows why the Magic Marble Messengers do things this way. Also, the Magic Marbles are so valuable that many children do not use all their Magic Marbles in any one year and may save some for the next year.

This means that every year, some children start with leftover marbles and some don't. On the first night of the year, each child finds out how many marbles they will receive each night for 30 nights.

Here are some examples of how many Magic Marbles three different children on Rhomaar received, including how many Magic Marbles they had left over from the year before. As you listen to the stories, think about the number of Magic Marbles each child has after a few days, after a week, after two weeks, and so on. Of course, one question that these Rhomaarian children think about often is this: At the end of the first 30 days of the year, when they can start to spend their Magic Marbles, how many Magic Marbles will they have?①

Teaching Note

① **Interpreting "Marbles Received Each Night" and "Total Marbles on Day 1"** The Magic Marbles are left each night, so that by the next day the Rhomaar child has the marbles. Therefore, on "Day 1," the child has already received his or her first batch of marbles. For example, Franick starts with 30 marbles and receives 3 each night. That means *before Day 1*, Franick already has 30 marbles. The night before Day 1, she receives 3 marbles, so on Day 1 she has 33 marbles. That night she again receives 3 marbles, so on Day 2 she has 36 marbles. Note that this has actually *not* turned out to be a source of confusion for students; they seem to readily understand this scenario.

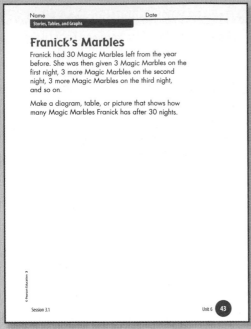

▲ **Student Activity Book, p. 43**

As you refer to each child in the next part of the story, show the corresponding part of the chart you prepared for this session.

Child	Beginning number of marbles	Nightly number of marbles
Franick	30	3
Bolar	0	5
Zupin	60	2

Franick had 30 Magic Marbles left from the year before. She was given three Magic Marbles on the first night, three more Magic Marbles on the second night, three more Magic Marbles on the third night, and so on for 30 nights.

Bolar had no leftover Magic Marbles from the year before. He was given five Magic Marbles on the first night, five more Magic Marbles on the second night, five more Magic Marbles on the third night, and so on.

Zupin had 60 Magic Marbles from the year before. She was given two Magic Marbles on the first night, two more Magic Marbles on the second night, two more Magic Marbles on the third night, and so on.

Make sure that all students understand this situation—how each child receives the same number of marbles each night for 30 nights. Ask whether they have some beginning ideas about who will have the most and fewest Magic Marbles by the end of the thirty days and why. Let them know that this problem is a complicated one and that they probably do not have enough evidence yet to figure it out. Tell students that they will be working together to solve this problem in the next activity.

ACTIVITY

② Representing Marble Stories

25 MIN   PAIRS

Each pair of students now works on only one of the three pages—*Student Activity Book* pages 43, 44, or 45. Assign one of the three pages to each pair so that there will be roughly equal numbers of representations for each of the three children of Rhomaar.

Explain that students should find a way to show the number of marbles received by their Rhomaarian child over the 30 nights.

Each of you now has the story of one of the Rhomaarian children I just told you about. Your task is to make a diagram, a table, or some kind of a picture that would help you keep track of how many Magic Marbles your assigned Rhomaarian child received after one night, two nights, three nights, four nights, all the way up to 30 nights. Then use the diagram, table, or picture you make to tell how many Magic Marbles this child has by the end of 30 nights. As you are thinking about ways to make your representation, share ideas with your partner.

You will have 25 minutes to make your representation, so focus on a clear way to show how the number of marbles increases without too much extra decoration.

You can remind students about other work they did when they developed representations and showed information in a clear and organized way so that others can understand it.

Students who do not complete their representations can finish them for homework. It is important that enough time is given to the discussion; students can participate even if their representation is partially completed.

Kelley and Dwayne's Work

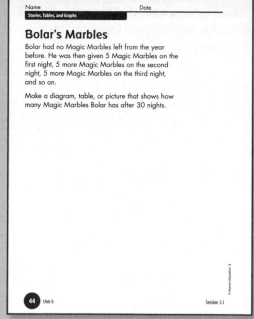

▲ **Student Activity Book, p. 44**

▲ **Student Activity Book, p. 45**

Professional Development

❷ **Teacher Note:** Students' Representations of Change, p. 126

ONGOING ASSESSMENT: Observing Students at Work

Students develop a way to represent a situation in which there is a starting amount (the leftover marbles) and a constant increase (a certain number of marbles per night).

- **What kinds of representations do students make?** Are their representations clear enough that someone else can interpret them?

- **Do they take into account the beginning number of marbles and the nightly number?**

- **Do their representations show the total for each day?**

As students work on their diagrams, tables, or pictures, look for three or four that can be shared at the end of this session as examples of the range of ways students in your class chose to represent this situation. Depending on how you have decided to have students share their work, select a few students to sketch their representations on an overhead transparency or on the board.❷

DIFFERENTIATION: Supporting the Range of Learners

Intervention Students who make a line graph as their representation usually need more time to finish than other students because of the detail needed to plot points. You may not have any students who try to make a line graph (these will be introduced in Session 3.4), but some students may realize that they can use the same method they used for graphing temperature in Investigation 1. Keep in mind that students need not complete their representations before the discussion. You can use an example of an unfinished line graph in the discussion and ask students to talk about how they think it would look if it were finished.

Extension If some pairs finish making their diagrams, tables, or pictures, they can share their work with another pair of students who have worked on the story of the *same* Rhomaarian child. They can compare their totals of the number of Magic Marbles after 30 days and explain how they figured that out by referring to their representation.

DISCUSSION

③ Comparing Representations

25 MIN   CLASS

Math Focus Points for Discussion

◆ Describing the relationship between two quantities in a situation with a constant rate of change, taking into account a beginning amount and a constant increase

◆ Comparing different representations that show the same situation

For your reference, see the provided table of nightly Magic Marble increases for Franick, Bolar, and Zupin (M22).

Ask students you have identified to show their representations on the board or overhead. During this discussion, emphasize that there are many ways to represent this situation. Ask students what features of each representation help them see and understand how the number of marbles grows over the 30 nights. Start out by asking some general questions about each representation.

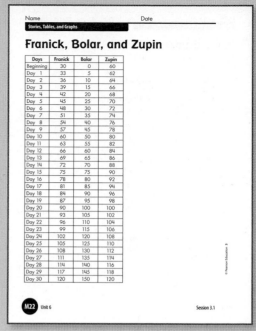

Franick, Bolar, and Zupin

Days	Franick	Bolar	Zupin
Beginning	30	0	60
Day 1	33	5	62
Day 2	36	10	64
Day 3	39	15	66
Day 4	42	20	68
Day 5	45	25	70
Day 6	48	30	72
Day 7	51	35	74
Day 8	54	40	76
Day 9	57	45	78
Day 10	60	50	80
Day 11	63	55	82
Day 12	66	60	84
Day 13	69	65	86
Day 14	72	70	88
Day 15	75	75	90
Day 16	78	80	92
Day 17	81	85	94
Day 18	84	90	96
Day 19	87	95	98
Day 20	90	100	100
Day 21	93	105	102
Day 22	96	110	104
Day 23	99	115	106
Day 24	102	120	108
Day 25	105	125	110
Day 26	108	130	112
Day 27	111	135	114
Day 28	114	140	116
Day 29	117	145	118
Day 30	120	150	120

M22 Unit 6   Session 3.1

▲ **Resource Masters, M22**

Number of marbles Each Night	Night	Total Marbles
2 ×	1	2
2 ×	2	4
2 ×	3	6
2 ×	4	8

Left Over	Number of marbles Each Night	Total
60	2	62
	2	64
	2	66
	2	68

Sample Student Work

How does this representation show how the number of marbles grows? What can you tell clearly? Do you have any questions about how [Beatriz] and [Nicholas] made their picture?

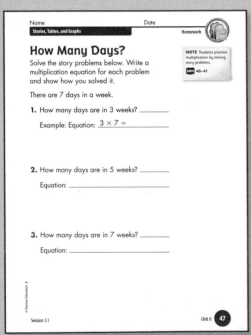

▲ **Student Activity Book, p. 46**

▲ **Student Activity Book, p. 47**

Follow up with more specific questions, such as these:

Where did [Edwin] show the beginning number of marbles? How did [Ines] keep track of the way the total number changed every day? Who can say in their own words how [Dwayne] figured out the total amount at the end of 30 days?

Also ask questions about comparing different representations.

What is the same about how [Edwin] and [Ines] thought about Franick's marbles? What is different?

Some students may begin to notice how the growth of the three children's total marbles compares over time. Acknowledge how important these ideas are, but put off this part of the discussion until the next session, when these ideas will be the focus.

SESSION FOLLOW-UP

④ Daily Practice and Homework

 Daily Practice: For ongoing review, have students complete *Student Activity Book* page 46.

Homework: Students practice multiplication by solving problems about the number of days in weeks on *Student Activity Book* page 47.

Student Math Handbook: Students and families may use *Student Math Handbook* pages 75–80 for reference and review. See pages 156–161 in the back of this unit.

Working with Tables

Math Focus Points

◆ Using tables to represent the relationship between two quantities in a situation with a constant rate of change

◆ Interpreting numbers in a table in terms of the situation they represent

◆ Comparing situations by describing differences in the tables that represent them

◆ Making rules that relate one variable to the other in situations with a constant rate of change

Vocabulary
column
row
table

Today's Plan			Materials
DISCUSSION **① Introducing Tables: Comparing Franick and Bolar**	20 MIN	CLASS	• T84–T85 • Chart paper*
ACTIVITY **② Tables That Go by 5s**	25 MIN	PAIRS	• *Student Activity Book,* pp. 49–51 • Chart: "Rhomaarian Children" class chart* (from Session 3.1); table of Tovar's Marbles*
DISCUSSION **③ What's the Rule for Tovar?**	15 MIN	CLASS	• *Student Activity Book,* pp. 49–51
SESSION FOLLOW-UP **④ Daily Practice**			• *Student Activity Book,* p. 52 • *Student Math Handbook,* pp. 81–86

*See *Materials to Prepare,* p. 75.

Ten-Minute Math

Today's Number Write the following expressions that equal 300 on the board and have students solve them: $27 + 100 + 73 + 200 - 100$; $(50 \times 3) + (50 \times 4) - 50$; $(100 \times 4) \div 2 + 100$; $400 - (10 \times 10)$

For each expression, ask students these questions:

• Which operations appear in the expression?

• How did you solve the problem?

If time remains, ask students to create their own expressions that equal 300.

Stories, Tables, and Graphs

Table for Franick and Bolar (page 1 of 2)

	DAY	FRANICK	BOLAR
	Beginning	30	0
WEEK 1	Day 1	33	5
	Day 2	36	10
	Day 3	39	15
	Day 4	42	20
	Day 5	45	25
	Day 6	48	30
	Day 7	51	35
WEEK 2	Day 8		
	Day 9		
	Day 10		
	Day 11		
	Day 12		
	Day 13		
	Day 14		

T84

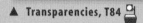

▲ **Transparencies, T84**

DISCUSSION

① Introducing Tables: Comparing Franick and Bolar

20 MIN CLASS

Math Focus Points for Discussion

◆ Using tables to represent the relationship between two quantities in a situation with a constant rate of change

◆ Interpreting numbers in a table in terms of the situation they represent

◆ Comparing situations by describing differences in the tables that represent them

Show the transparency of Table for Franick and Bolar (T84), or draw students' attention to the table you have prepared on chart paper with the data for Week 1 filled in. If some students created representations similar to tables in Session 3.1, point out the similarity of these representations. Let students know that this kind of representation is called a table.

Students use tables to represent the relationship between two quantities in a situation of constant change.

Students worked with tables in Grade 2, but they may need some review of what a table is and how it shows related pieces of information. Make sure that students can read the table and understand how the information in the table is arranged. Help students read the headings of the two columns, and ask them to tell you what they think the table shows. Use the words *row* and *column* to help students communicate clearly about the table. To check on students' understanding of the table, ask questions such as:

What information does this row of the table give about Day 4? What does this number, 42, mean? What about this number, 20? Can someone say a sentence about Franick and Bolar on Day 4 by looking at this row of the table?

If needed, you can start a sentence about a row of the table "On Day 4, Franick has . . ." You may also need to clarify that the total on Day 4 means the total after the child receives the nightly marbles, so the total for Day 4 includes the marbles received that night. As students work with tables in the rest of the Investigation, focus on helping them make connections between the information in the table and the situation it represents.

Now ask students what they notice about what is happening during Week 1.❶

What do you notice about Franick's and Bolar's marbles during Week 1? Do you see any patterns? How would you describe what is happening as the week goes on?

Ask students to help you fill in the data for Week 2 and repeat the same questions. In particular, ask students to compare the total number of marbles of the two children.

What do you notice about Franick's and Bolar's marbles? Do you see any patterns? How would you describe what is happening as the week goes on? Bolar started with no marbles saved from last year. Is Bolar's total staying below Franick's? What do you think is going to happen in Week 3?

Show the transparency of Table for Franick and Bolar (T85). With students' help, add Week 3 and then the rest of the 30 days, with some discussion of each period of time.

When the table is complete, focus on the total marbles for Franick and Bolar.

Who ended up with more marbles? Can you explain how that happened?❷ ❸

Teaching Note

❶ **How Many Days in a Week?** You may want to review that there are seven days in a week—the five days they go to school and the two weekend days.

Professional Development

❷ **Dialogue Box:** "He's Taking Bigger Steps, So He'll Catch Up", p. 149

❸ **Teacher Note:** Using and Interpreting Tables, p. 128

Stories, Tables, and Graphs

Table for Franick and Bolar (page 2 of 2)

	DAY	FRANICK	BOLAR
	Day 15		
	Day 16		
	Day 17		
WEEK 3	Day 18		
	Day 19		
	Day 20		
	Day 21		
	Day 22		
	Day 23		
	Day 24		
WEEK 4	Day 25		
	Day 26		
	Day 27		
	Day 28		
WEEK 5	Day 29		
	Day 30		

T85

▲ **Transparencies, T85**

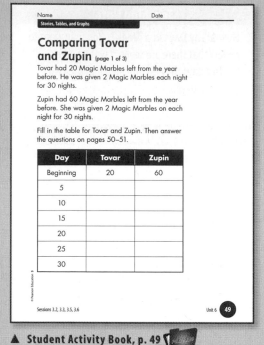

▲ Student Activity Book, p. 49

ACTIVITY

2 Tables That Go by 5s

25 MIN   PAIRS

Introduce students to the new Rhomaarian child, Tovar, whom you have added to the "Rhomaarian Children" class chart. Point out his starting amount (20) and nightly amount of marbles (2).

Child	Beginning number of marbles	Nightly number of marbles
Franick	30	3
Bolar	0	5
Zupin	60	2
Tovar	20	2

Briefly introduce tables in which the rows increase by five nights at a time by showing students the table you prepared showing Day 5 and Day 10 for Tovar:

TOVAR	
Beginning	20
Day 5	
Day 10	

After the children on Rhomaar get their first night's marbles, they know how many they will receive each night. They can then figure out how many marbles they will have by the end of the 30 nights. They use tables, too, but they don't record the number of marbles for every night. They want to determine more efficiently and quickly the number of Magic Marbles they have without figuring out the number for every day. They just use the Starting Amount (the marbles left over from last year), then Day 5, Day 10, Day 15, and so on. Here's the beginning of a table for Tovar. How would you figure out how many marbles Tovar has on Day 5 without writing in the numbers for Days 1, 2, 3, and 4?

Take a few suggestions from students, but do not have a long discussion about this idea now. Students will work on their own and then have a longer discussion in the next session after they have had some experience with the new tables.

Students work in pairs on *Student Activity Book* pages 49–51, but each student records on his or her own sheet.

ONGOING ASSESSMENT: Observing Students at Work

Students determine how to find the total accumulation of marbles on any day, taking into account a starting amount and a constant increase. They compare two situations with different starting amounts and the same constant change.

- **How do students figure out the number of marbles on Days 5, 10, 15, and so on?** Do they compute each intervening day? Do they come up with a rule for finding the number of marbles on any day?

- **What do they notice when they compare Tovar and Zupin?** Do they notice that the difference between the number of marbles is the same on any day? Can they explain why this is the case?

DISCUSSION

③ What's the Rule for Tovar?

15 MIN CLASS

Math Focus Points for Discussion

◆ Comparing situations by describing differences in the tables that represent them

◆ Making rules that relate one variable to the other in situations with a constant rate of change

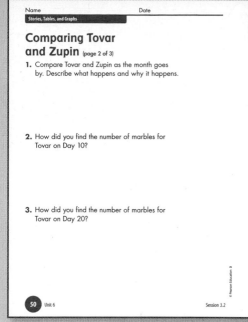

▲ **Student Activity Book, p. 50**

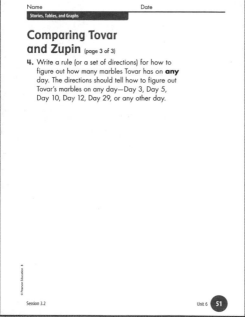

▲ **Student Activity Book, p. 51**

First ask students what they found out about Zupin and Tovar.

What happened over the course of the 30 days? How did Zupin's and Tovar's totals compare? Can you explain what you noticed in terms of the Beginning Number and Nightly Number of Marbles each child received?

Day	Tovar	Zupin
Beginning	20	60
5	30	70
10	40	80
15	50	90
20	60	100
25	70	110
30	80	120

Sample Student Work

Students will probably notice that, unlike the situation in which they compared Franick and Bolar in which one child caught up, Tovar does not catch up to Zupin, and the difference between Tovar and Zupin does not change.

Students might say:

"They both go by 10s."

"Zupin starts ahead and she stays ahead all the way."

"She has to stay ahead because they just always get the same—it's always 2, 2, 2, and she started with more."

"Tovar can never catch up unless he starts getting more than Zupin."

After a few minutes of discussion, ask students about the first question on the student sheet.

Who has a strategy for figuring out Tovar's total marbles for Day 10 without figuring out all the days up until Day 10? What about for Day 20?

Ask students to share and explain their strategies. As the discussion progresses, encourage students to articulate a rule (or a method or a set of directions) about how many marbles Tovar has on any day. Record students' statements of their rule or directions on the board in words; for example, "You always start with 20 and then you add on two for each day." Ask follow-up questions such as "Why do you always start with 20?" **❹**

Then ask students to use their rules to figure out the marble total for Tovar for other days. Have them work in pairs for a few minutes on one of the following questions:

Using your rules, how would you figure out how many marbles Tovar had on the 12th day without looking back at your chart? How about the 15th day? What if the children received Magic Marbles for 10 extra days? Can anyone say how you'd figure out Tovar's number of marbles for 40 days?

After students have worked for a few minutes, ask them how they solved the problem.

If you have additional time, you can ask about a rule for Zupin for the number of marbles she has on any day.

Professional Development

❹ Dialogue Box: Why Are There Five 2s?, p. 151

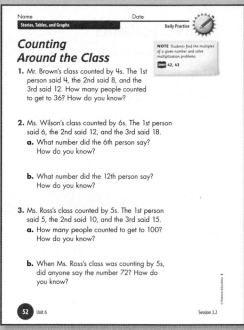

Counting Around the Class

NOTE Students find the multiples of a given number and solve multiplication problems.

SMH 42, 43

1. Mr. Brown's class counted by 4s. The 1st person said 4, the 2nd said 8, and the 3rd said 12. How many people counted to get to 36? How do you know?

2. Ms. Wilson's class counted by 6s. The 1st person said 6, the 2nd said 12, and the 3rd said 18.
   a. What number did the 6th person say? How do you know?
   b. What number did the 12th person say? How do you know?

3. Ms. Ross's class counted by 5s. The 1st person said 5, the 2nd said 10, and the 3rd said 15.
   a. How many people counted to get to 100? How do you know?
   b. When Ms. Ross's class was counting by 5s, did anyone say the number 72? How do you know?

52 Unit 6   Session 3.2

▲ **Student Activity Book, p. 52**

SESSION FOLLOW-UP

 4 Daily Practice

 Daily Practice: For ongoing review, have students complete *Student Activity Book* page 52.

 Student Math Handbook: Students and families may use *Student Math Handbook* pages 81–86 for reference and review. See pages 156–161 in the back of this unit.

Describing a Rule

Math Focus Points

◆ Interpreting numbers in a table in terms of the situation they represent

◆ Making rules that relate one variable to the other in situations with a constant rate of change

◆ Connecting the steps of a general method or rule to the parts of the situation they represent

Today's Plan		Materials
ACTIVITY **①** **Using a Table to Compare**	30 MIN PAIRS	• *Student Activity Book,* p. 49 (from Session 3.2), 53–55 • Chart: "Rhomaarian Children" class chart* (from Session 3.1); calculators (optional)
DISCUSSION **②** **Finding Rules for Any Day**	30 MIN CLASS	• *Student Activity Book,* pp. 53–55
SESSION FOLLOW-UP **③** **Daily Practice and Homework**		• *Student Activity Book,* pp. 56–57 • *Student Math Handbook,* p. 87

*See *Materials to Prepare,* p. 75.

Ten-Minute Math

Today's Number Students create expressions that equal 38. They must use at least two operations and each expression must start with a number greater than 100; for example: $158 - 20 - (25 \times 4) = 38$. Collect a few expressions to write on the board and ask students which part of the problem they solved first and what strategy they used to the rest of the class.

ACTIVITY

1 Using a Table to Compare

30 MIN   PAIRS

Tell students that today they will be looking at two new Rhomaarian children, Winger and Jorad. They will also be looking back at Tovar. Show students the addition of Winger and Jorad to the "Rhomaarian Children" chart.

Child	Beginning number of marbles	Nightly number of marbles
Tovar	20	2
Winger	20	4
Jorad	45	3

Students work on *Student Activity Book* pages 53–55. They work in pairs, but each student fills in his or her own copy of the *Student Activity Book*. Students can copy the data for Tovar from *Student Activity Book* page 49, which they completed in Session 3.2.

As the *Student Activity Book* page 53 indicates, students complete the table for Winger and Tovar first and leave the column for Jorad blank for now. Then they answer Questions 1 through 3 on *Student Activity Book* page 54 and Question 4 on *Student Activity Book* page 55. Students will have additional time to fill in the data for Jorad in the next session.

ONGOING ASSESSMENT: Observing Students at Work

Students complete a table showing every five days of marble accumulation for three Rhomarian children. They compare two situations of constant change that have the same starting amounts but different constant increases.

- **How do students figure out the number of marbles on Days 5, 10, 15, and so on?** Do they compute each intervening day? Do they come up with a rule for any day?

- **Do students notice that the difference between Tovar and Winger's number of marbles gets bigger and bigger?** Can they explain why this is true?

- **Do students notice that the difference between Winger and Jorad gradually decreases?** Can they explain why this is true?

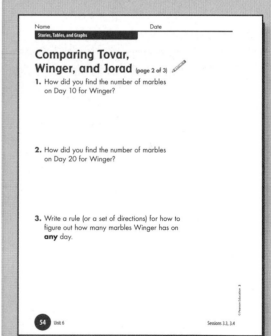

Name _____ **Date** _____
Stories, Tables, and Graphs

Comparing Tovar, Winger, and Jorad (page 1 of 3)

Tovar had 20 Magic Marbles left from the year before. He was then given 2 Magic Marbles each night for 30 nights.

Winger had 20 Magic Marbles left from the year before. She was then given 4 Magic Marbles on each night for 30 nights.

Jorad had 45 Magic Marbles left from the year before. She was then given 3 Magic Marbles on each night for 30 nights.

Fill in the table for Tovar and Winger. The table shows how many marbles they have after every 5 nights. (Do **not** fill in Jorad's yet.)

Day	Tovar	Winger	Jorad
Beginning	20	20	45
5			
10			
15			
20			
25			
30			

Sessions 3.3, 3.4, 3.5   Unit 6 53

▲ **Student Activity Book, p. 53**

Name _____ **Date** _____
Stories, Tables, and Graphs

Comparing Tovar, Winger, and Jorad (page 2 of 3)

1. How did you find the number of marbles on Day 10 for Winger?

2. How did you find the number of marbles on Day 20 for Winger?

3. Write a rule (or a set of directions) for how to figure out how many marbles Winger has on **any** day.

54 Unit 6   Sessions 3.3, 3.4

▲ **Student Activity Book, pp. 54–55**

Math Note

❶ **Using Calculators** Figuring out the number of marbles for Jorad is a good example of a problem in which a calculator is useful for third graders. The focus of this problem is the relationship between three quantities—the starting number of marbles, the constant increase, and the total number of marbles on a particular day. In order to use the calculator, students must think through how these three quantities are related and how to apply addition and multiplication to solve the problem. At other times, students learn about and practice computation without a calculator, but here they can use the calculator to carry out computations while they focus on the structure of the problem. Look for other opportunities in the classroom for students to use a calculator when the purpose of the mathematical activity is not the development of computational skills and when the numbers and calculations are not yet accessible to students' level of written or mental computation. **Part 5: Technology in** *Investigations:* **Calculators and Computers** in *Implementing Investigations in Grade 3:* Using Calculators with the Curriculum.

DIFFERENTIATION: Supporting the Range of Learners

Extension Students who finish the work on Tovar and Winger can complete the table for Jorad and answer Questions 5 and 6 on *Student Activity Book* page 55. Completing the table for Jorad is more difficult than for any other Rhomaarian child in this Investigation because of the combination of higher numbers and a less familiar number sequence. Students may use calculators to figure out their totals or check their calculations for this sequence.❶

Students who complete all the work on *Student Activity Book* pages 53–55 can work on finding a rule for the number of marbles Jorad has on any day as an additional challenge.

DISCUSSION

30 MIN   CLASS

② Finding Rules for Any Day

Math Focus Points for Discussion

◆ Making rules that relate one variable to the other in situations with a constant rate of change

◆ Connecting the steps of a general method or rule to the parts of the situation they represent

Students need their copies of *Student Activity Book* pages 53–55. First, ask students what they noticed from the table for Tovar and Winger:

Now, looking at the number of marbles for Tovar and Winger, can anyone tell the story of how the number of Magic Marbles changes during the month? How did Tovar and Winger compare at the beginning? What happens as the month goes on? Can you explain why this happens?

Day	Tovar	Winger
Beginning	20	20
5	30	40
10	40	60
15	50	80
20	60	100
25	70	120
30	80	140

Then ask students how they figured out the number of marbles on certain days for Winger.

How did you figure out Day 10 for Winger? How did you figure out Day 20 for Winger? Can you tell how many Magic Marbles Winger receives every 5 nights? How do you know?❷

Students might say:

"For Day 20, I knew that it went up 20 each time, so I counted by 20s."

"Every day she gets 4, so I knew that for 5 days, it's 5 times 4."

"I just did 20 × 4 and then added on the 20 from the start."

Help students clarify their methods and how they take into account both the starting number of marbles and the constant increase. Ask other students to restate and explain some of these ideas.

[Ines] said that she knew that it was 20 each time. Who can explain what that 20 represents?

Why would [Benjamin] multiply 20 by 4? Why did he add 20 more?

After hearing some strategies, ask students to turn over the chart and ask about a day that is not on it.❸

Turn your charts over for a minute and think about this problem. Let's say that we want to find the number of marbles for Day 6 for Winger. Remember that she starts with 20 and then gets four marbles each night. How many marbles does she have on Day 6?

Ask students to work in pairs briefly on this problem, and then collect their responses and methods. Record several of these. Then ask whether these methods can be used to find the total number of marbles for Winger for any day. Record students' methods on the board and ask students to make them as clear as they can.❹

Differentiation

❷ **English Language Learners** To clarify the meaning of *rule* in this context, you can explain to English Language Learners that a rule in this case means "a set of directions or steps." To reinforce this idea, you can review some of the steps students described during the discussion (e.g., "I just did 20 × 4 and then added on the 20 from the start"). Write out the words, and help English Language Learners figure out what the 20 and the 4 represent.

Math Note

❸ **Number Sequences and General Methods** Students often use the pattern of increase that they see to fill in the table. For example, after they have filled in one or two rows, they see that Winger's marbles increase by 20 every five days. Some students easily fill in the counting pattern they know—20, 40, 60, 80, 100, . . .—and lose track of what these numbers represent and how the constant increase is related to the number of days. By working on a day that is not a multiple of five without using their chart, they must think through again how the starting amount and the constant increase are related to the total number of marbles. This thinking can lead to more general methods of finding the total number of marbles for any day—methods that do not depend on knowing a previous total.

Teaching Note

❹ **Rule, Method, Procedure, Plan** Help students understand that they are trying to find a general method that works to find the number of marbles for *any* number of days. Sometimes students do not understand what *rule* means in this context. The words *method* or *procedure* may be more familiar. One student called the steps that work for any day a "thinking plan."

▲ **Student Activity Book, p. 56**

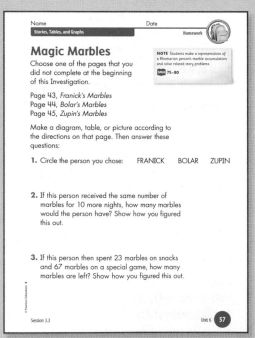

▲ **Student Activity Book, p. 57**

Throughout this discussion, emphasize how the parts of each method correspond to what is going on in the marble situation.

[Gil]'s method is to multiply the number of days by 4 and then add 20. What does the 4 represent? What about the 20? [Deondra]'s method is to start with 20 and then add 24. Can you explain to us where the 24 came from? Could we use [Gil]'s method to find the number of marbles for a different number of days? What about [Deondra]'s method?

Now ask students to work in pairs for a few minutes on some other days that are not on the chart.

Without looking back at your tables, can you use your rules or methods to figure out how many marbles Winger has on Day 11? Day 9? Day 12? Day 18?

If you have additional time, students can continue working on *Student Activity Book* pages 53–55, filling in the table for Jorad and answering Questions 5 and 6. Students will need their work from *Student Activity Book* pages 53–55 for the next session.

SESSION FOLLOW-UP

3 Daily Practice and Homework

 Daily Practice: For ongoing review, have students complete *Student Activity Book* page 56.

 Homework: Students make a representation of marble accumulation for one of the Rhomaarian children they did not work on in Session 3.1 and answer questions about the number of marbles they have on *Student Activity Book* page 57.

 Student Math Handbook: Students and families may use *Student Math Handbook* page 87 for reference and review. See pages 156–161 in the back of this unit.

Making Graphs from Tables

Math Focus Points

◆ Connecting the steps of a general method or rule to the parts of the situation they represent

◆ Plotting points on a graph to represent a situation in which one quantity is changing in relation to another

◆ Identifying points on a graph with corresponding values in a table and interpreting the numerical information in terms of the situation the graph represents

Today's Plan		Materials
DISCUSSION **❶ Rules for Jorad**	15 MIN CLASS	• *Student Activity Book,* p. 53 (from Session 3.3) • Calculator (optional)
ACTIVITY **❷ Making a Graph from a Table**	45 MIN CLASS PAIRS	• *Student Activity Book,* pp. 53–55 (from Session 3.3), 59–60, 61–63 • T86 🖨; M26* • Chart: "Rhomaarian Children" class chart (from Session 3.1); chart paper* (optional); Colored pencils or crayons (optional)
SESSION FOLLOW-UP **❸ Daily Practice**		• *Student Activity Book,* p. 64 • *Student Math Handbook,* pp. 75–80, 81–86, 87

*See *Materials to Prepare,* p. 75.

Ten-Minute Math

Today's Number   Write the following expressions that equal 125 on the board and have students solve them: $(4 \times 25) + 50 - 25$; $(200 \div 2) + 75 - 50$; $38 + 62 + (100 \div 4)$; $13 + 12 + (2 \times 50)$

For each expression, ask students these questions:

• Which operations appear in the expression?

• How many operations are in the expression?

• How did you solve the problem?

If time remains, ask students to create their own expressions that equal 125.

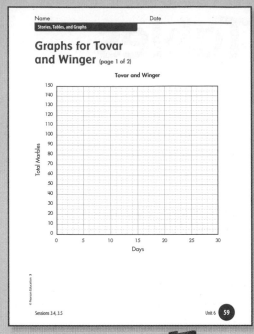

▲ **Student Activity Book, p. 59**

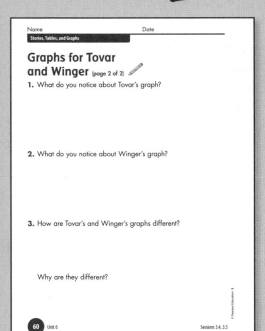

▲ **Student Activity Book, p. 60**

DISCUSSION

1 Rules for Jorad

15 MIN   CLASS

Math Focus Points for Discussion

◆ Connecting the steps of a general method or rule to the parts of the situation they represent

If needed, give students a few minutes to complete filling in the data for Jorad on *Student Activity Book* page 53.

Ask students how they figured out the number of marbles on certain days for Jorad.

How did you figure out Day 10 for Jorad? How did you figure out Day 20 for Jorad? Can you tell how many Magic Marbles Jorad receives every five nights? How do you know?

Day	Jorad
Beginning	45
5	60
10	75
15	90
20	105
25	120
30	135

After hearing some strategies, ask students to articulate a rule to find the total number of marbles for Jorad for any day. Record students' methods on the board and ask students to make them as clear as they can. Throughout this discussion, emphasize how the parts of each method correspond to what is going on in the marble situation.

Then ask about some days that are not on the chart.

Without looking back at your tables, can you use your rules to figure out how many marbles Jorad has on Day 6? Day 9? Day 12? Day 18? You don't need to come up with the actual number of marbles. I want to hear what you would do—what steps you would take—to find the total.

Ask students to work in pairs for a few minutes on one of these problems. Then ask them to explain what method they used. Because the numbers for Jorad are difficult, encourage students to explain *how* they would calculate the number of marbles for a particular day without necessarily doing all the calculations. For example, Day 12 requires multiplying 12 by 3 and then adding 45. Articulating these steps shows that the student knows how to apply the general rule for Jorad, even if the actual total of 81 marbles has not been calculated. So that students can focus on how to use the starting amount and the constant increase to find the total number of marbles, you may say, "You tell me what to do and I'll be your calculator," or you can have one student actually use a calculator to carry out the calculations.

Students might say:

"You could use a number line and skip 15, but you have to start at 45."

"You start with 45 and you jump 3 for every day."

"I did it differently. You just times 3 by the number of days. Then at the end you add 45."

"You can add on 15 for every 5 days. Then just see how many more days. For Day 12, it's 15 and 15 because there's two fives, that's 30. Then add on 3 and 3. So it's 36 for the days, and then add on the marbles she had at the start."

Record students' methods as they explain them, using their own words. Make sure that they can indicate what each number means. ❶

Method for Jorad

Start with 45. Add on 3 for each day.

3 × number of days + 45

15 for every 5 days. 3 for any leftover days. Add 45.

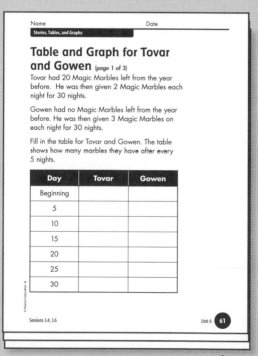

▲ **Student Activity Book, pp. 61–63** WRITING

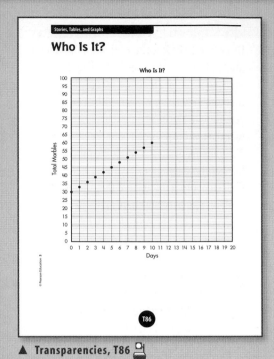

Stories, Tables, and Graphs

Who Is It?

Who Is It?

[graph titled "Who Is It?" with vertical axis "Total Marbles" from 0 to 100 and horizontal axis "Days" from 0 to 20, showing plotted points rising from about 30 at day 0 to about 60 at day 10]

T86

▲ **Transparencies, T86**

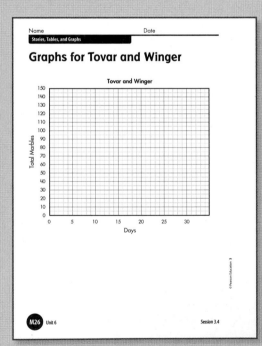

Name _____ Date _____

Stories, Tables, and Graphs

Graphs for Tovar and Winger

Tovar and Winger

[blank grid graph with vertical axis "Total Marbles" from 0 to 150 and horizontal axis "Days" from 0 to 30]

M26 Unit 6   Session 3.4

▲ **Resource Masters, M26**

ACTIVITY

2 Making a Graph from a Table

45 MIN   CLASS   PAIRS

Remind students that in Investigation 1, they used graphs to show how temperature changed over a period of time. You can refer to the temperature graph in your classroom. Then show them the transparency (or the graph on chart paper) of Who Is It? (T86), which shows Franick's accumulation of marbles for the first ten days (do not tell students that this graph represents Franick).

Do you remember how we used graphs to show how temperature changes over a period of time? Now we're going to use graphs again to look at how the total number of marbles is changing for some of the Rhomaarian children. We've used tables to compare different children. Now we're going to see how graphs can help us compare.

Here's a graph that gives some information about one of the Rhomaarian children we have on our class chart. If you think you know who it is, don't say anything yet. I'll ask you that in a minute. But without saying the name of a child, what can you say about what this graph shows?

Ask follow-up questions about the graph. Focus on the meaning of the numbers along the horizontal and vertical axes and on what particular points on the graph show.

What do the numbers along the horizontal axis show? What do the numbers along the vertical axis show? What does this point mean? What does the point on the graph right above 0 on the horizontal axis mean?

It is important for students to see that a point on this graph shows a relationship between two kinds of information—the day and the total number of marbles—just as the temperature graphs show a relationship between a day and a temperature. A follow-up question to help with the meaning of a point on the graph may be this:

Who can say a sentence about this point on the graph that includes some information about days and some information about the total number of marbles?

In particular, make sure that students understand that the point at 0 Days shows the beginning number of marbles (the marbles left over from the previous year).

Now ask students to look at the "Rhomaarian Children" chart and come up with an idea about which child the graph shows. You may have students talk in pairs for a minute about this. Ask students for their idea of who the child is and what evidence they see on the graph. Then let students know that the marble increase continues in the same way, as for all children of Rhomaar, and have students help you plot several more points on the graph. Go over carefully how to plot a point by finding the day on the horizontal axis and the number of marbles on the vertical axis.❷

Does this remind you of our temperature graph? Does that help you know where to put the points on this graph? Is there anything confusing to you about how we have put the points on the graph so far?

Tell students that they will be making Graphs for Tovar and Winger (M26). They should keep track of anything that is difficult or confusing about making the graphs so that the class can discuss any difficulties together at the end of the session.

Students turn to *Student Activity Book* pages 59–60. They will also need their table on *Student Activity Book* page 53 from Session 3.3.

Tell students to graph Tovar first. When Tovar's graph is complete, they can graph Winger on the same set of axes.❸ ❹ ❺

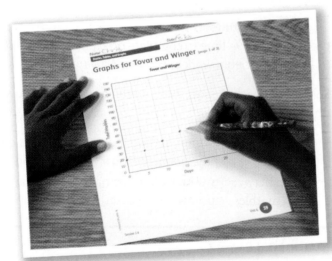

Students plot points on a graph to represent the relationship between the number of days and the total number of marbles.

When students finish the graphs for both Tovar and Winger, they should work on *Student Activity Book* page 60, answering questions about what the graphs show.

Math Note

❷ **Plotting Points on a Graph** Even though students have been using a temperature graph all year, there is usually still some confusion about how to plot a point that represents both a number of days and a number of marbles. Ask students what their strategies are for figuring out where the next point on the graph goes. Some students may put a finger on the day and a finger on the number of marbles and move their fingers up and to the right, respectively, until they touch. Other students may notice that they can use the previous point to plot the next point. For example, from the point for Day 10, they can move over one day to Day 11 and move up two spaces vertically for the two additional marbles. Also remind students of their experience of plotting points to show the temperature.

Teaching Note

❸ **Connecting the Points** Students often find it helpful to draw light lines connecting the points on their graphs and to use two different colors or symbols, one for Tovar and one for Winger. They can make a key to show which color or set of symbols stands for which child. The graphs for the marble situation are actually not lines, like the temperature graphs students worked on in Investigation 1, but a series of points. However, it is convenient to use a line to show the trend of the values on the graph. See **Teacher Note:** Graphs of Situations with a Constant Rate of Change, p. 130 for more information on discrete and continuous change.

Professional Development

❹ **Teacher Note:** Graphs of Situations with a Constant Rate of Change, p. 130

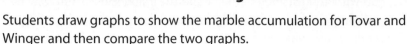

Math Note

❺ Two Points at the Same Location on a Graph
Some students do not know what to do when they need to start their graph for Winger on a point that is already "occupied" by a point for Tovar. Remind them that this sometimes happened on their temperature graphs—points from two different cities occupied the same point because it was the same temperature in those two cities on the same day. Ask students what it means that a point for Tovar is on the same place on the graph as a point for Winger.

Teaching Note

❻ Creating a Graph Remember that creating a graph that shows the relationship between two variables is more difficult than reading such a graph. Acknowledge that making these graphs can be confusing, help students plot points on their graphs, remind them that each point shows two pieces of information found on the axes, and encourage students to share what is difficult about these graphs in the class discussion. See **Teacher Note:** Using Line Graphs to Represent Change, p. 117.

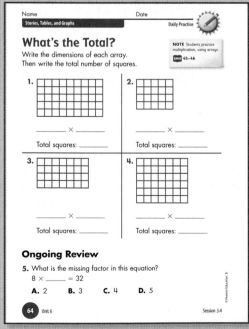

▲ **Student Activity Book, p. 64**

ONGOING ASSESSMENT: Observing Students at Work

Students draw graphs to show the marble accumulation for Tovar and Winger and then compare the two graphs.

- **Can students plot the graphs of the two sequences accurately?**

- **Can students read the graph, interpreting what each point means?**

- **Can students compare the two graphs?** Are they using language such as *steeper, goes up more slowly,* or *goes up faster* to describe the patterns of change?

These two linear sequences begin at the same point and then one increases more rapidly than the other.❻

As needed, provide additional copies of Graphs for Tovar and Winger (M26) if students need to start over.

DIFFERENTIATION: Supporting the Range of Learners

Intervention Ask students who understand how to plot points to help other students.

Extension Students who finish early can return to any questions they did not have time to complete on *Student Activity Book* pages 53–55 and/or begin work on *Student Activity Book* pages 61–63.

For additional challenge, students can answer the following question on blank paper:

- If Tovar and Winger kept getting the same amounts of marbles for 30 more days, would the graph for Tovar and the graph for Winger ever meet? Why or why not?

SESSION FOLLOW-UP

3 Daily Practice

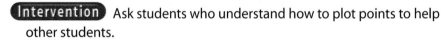

Daily Practice: For ongoing review, have students complete *Student Activity Book* page 64.

Student Math Handbook: Students and families may use *Student Math Handbook* pages 75–80, 81–86, 87 for reference and review. See pages 156–161 in the back of this unit.

Using Graphs to Compare

Math Focus Points

◆ Identifying points on a graph with corresponding values in a table and interpreting the numerical information in terms of the situation the graph represents

◆ Comparing situations by describing differences in their graphs

Today's Plan		Materials
① DISCUSSION **Telling a Story from a Graph** ⏱ 20 MIN 👥 CLASS		• *Student Activity Book,* pp. 53, 59–60 (from Session 3.4) • T87 🖨 • Chart paper (optional)*
② ACTIVITY **Using Graphs to Compare** ⏱ 40 MIN 👥 PAIRS		• *Student Activity Book,* p. 53 (from Session 3.4), 61–63, 65–67 • Chart: "Rhomaarian Children" class chart* (from Session 3.1); colored pencils or crayons (optional)
③ SESSION FOLLOW-UP **Daily Practice and Homework**		• *Student Activity Book,* pp. 68–69 • *Student Math Handbook,* pp. 75–80, 81–86

*See *Materials to Prepare,* p. 77.

Ten-Minute Math

Guess My Rule Choose the rule "Multiples of 4." Write three examples that fit this rule in a circle labeled "Follows My Rule." Students suggest numbers that may or may not fit this rule. Place them inside or outside the circle. Multiples of 4 are also multiples of 2, so encourage students to look carefully at the numbers outside the circle. If 6 (or 10) is not there, place it outside the circle and ask why that one does not fit. Encourage students to name the rule in any way they can; for example, "You name these numbers if you count by 4s."

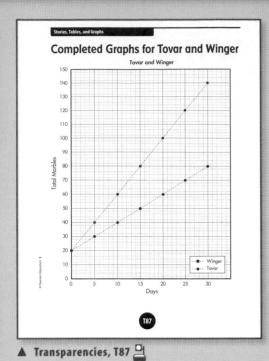

Stories, Tables, and Graphs

Completed Graphs for Tovar and Winger

Tovar and Winger

T87

▲ **Transparencies, T87**

DISCUSSION

Telling a Story from a Graph

20 MIN   CLASS

Math Focus Points for Discussion

◆ Identifying points on a graph with corresponding values in a table and interpreting the numerical information in terms of the situation the graph represents

◆ Comparing situations by describing differences in their graphs

Day	Tovar	Winger
Beginning	20	20
5	30	40
10	40	60
15	50	80
20	60	100
25	70	120
30	80	140

Students need *Student Activity Book* pages 59–60 for this discussion. However, students need not have finished answering all the questions on *Student Activity Book* page 60 before this discussion.

Use the transparency of Completed Graphs for Tovar and Winger (T87) or the large graph you made on chart paper for students to refer to during this discussion.

First talk with students about any confusion that came up as they plotted information from their tables onto the graph. To check students' understanding of the meaning of the graph, ask questions such as these:

What does this point mean? Who can say a sentence about this point on the graph that includes some information about days and some information about the total number of marbles?

Also make sure that students can connect the information in their table on *Student Activity Book* page 53, to the graph. Ask questions such as the following:

Look at this row of the table. Who can say a sentence about what this row of the table tells us about Tovar? Where is the point on the graph that gives the same information? Look at this point on the graph. Where can you find the same information in the table?

Then ask what the graphs show about Tovar's and Winger's marbles.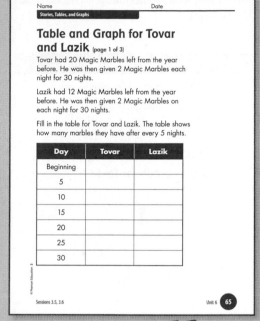

We've looked at tables before to tell the story of someone's marbles. Now we're going to see how we can see the story of the marbles from a graph. What do you notice about the points on the graph for Tovar? What do you notice about the points for Winger? How are they the same? How are they different? Who can show me with your hand how Tovar's graph goes and how Winger's graph goes? What does that show us about what's happening with the marbles?

Students often notice that, although they start with the same number of marbles, Tovar's and Winger's totals get farther and farther apart.

Students might say:

"Winger has more of an incline."

"At the beginning, when it's 20, there's none apart. But when you go up, it gets 10 more apart each time."

"They get farther and farther apart. I can't even spread my fingers to reach [the two points] on Day 30."

Students may describe one graph as "steeper" or as "going up faster." Continue to ask what their comments mean in terms of the situation, using the words they have come up with to describe the situation.

What does that tell us about the marbles? [Philip] says that Winger's line is going up faster. What does that mean? What is happening?

Follow-up questions may include these:

If Tovar and Winger kept getting the same number of marbles every night for 30 more days, what would the graphs look like? Will they ever intersect (cross each other)? How do you know?

Teaching Note

❶ Gestures The use of gestures has proven helpful in communicating about the general shape of the two graphs.

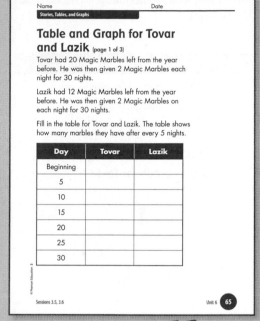

▲ Student Activity Book, p. 65

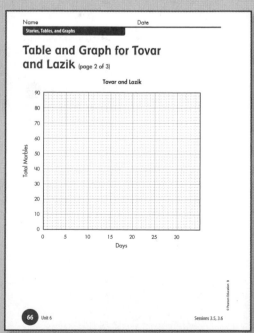

▲ Student Activity Book, p. 66

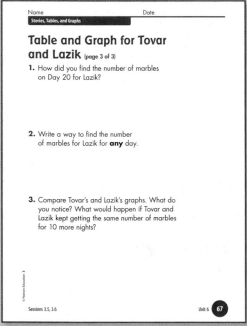

▲ **Student Activity Book, p. 67**

ACTIVITY
❷ Using Graphs to Compare

40 MIN   PAIRS

Introduce the two new Rhomaarian children, Gowen and Lazik. Show students the addition of these two children to the "Rhomaarian Children" class chart.

Child	Beginning number of marbles	Nightly number of marbles
Gowen	0	3
Lazik	12	2

Explain that students will compare Tovar with the new child, Gowen. They will fill in a chart for the number of marbles they have after every five nights and they will draw a graph for each child. Ask students how they think Gowen's graph may look, compared with, Tovar's.

Can you show with your hand how Tovar's graph goes? How do you think Gowen's graph will look, compared with Tovar's? Where will it start? Will it go up in the same way Tovar's does? How will it be different?

Students now complete *Student Activity Book* pages 61–63. They work in pairs but should complete their own student sheets. They can copy the values for Tovar from the table on *Student Activity Book* page 53. ❷ ❸

ONGOING ASSESSMENT: Observing Students at Work

Students determine how the total number of marbles changes for children with different starting amounts and rates of increase, draw graphs to show the marble accumulation for different pairs of children, and use the graphs to compare the two sequences.

- **Can students plot the graphs of the two sequences accurately?**

- **Can students read the graph, interpreting what each point means?**

- **Can students compare the two graphs?** Are they using language such as *steeper, goes up more slowly, goes up faster,* or *gets closer and closer* to describe the patterns of change?

As you circulate, ask students what they are noticing as they compare each pair of graphs.

> Who started with more marbles? Who ended up with more marbles? What happened as the month went on? Why do you think the two graphs for Tovar and Gowen cross? Then what happens?

Although Gowen begins with fewer marbles, he accumulates marbles at a greater rate, so his graph eventually intersects Tovar's.

DIFFERENTIATION: Supporting the Range of Learners

Intervention After you have given the directions, ask any students who are unsure about how to begin the graphs to stay with you in a small group. Work individually with these students to help them plot points and to review what each point means. Refer to their experience with graphing temperature to help them understand these graphs.

Extension Students who complete the graphs for Tovar and Gowen and answer the questions about these graphs can begin work on *Student Activity Book* pages 65–67, which they will continue working on in the next session.

SESSION FOLLOW-UP

3 Daily Practice and Homework

 Daily Practice: For ongoing review, have students complete *Student Activity Book* page 68.

 Homework: Students complete a table that shows constant change and solve a problem on *Student Activity Book* page 69.

 Student Math Handbook: Students and families may use *Student Math Handbook* pages 75–80, 81–86 for reference and review. See pages 156–161 in the back of this unit.

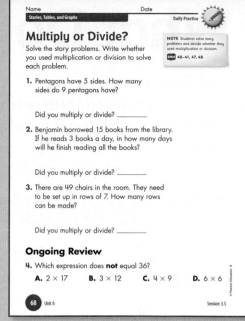

▲ **Student Activity Book, p. 68**

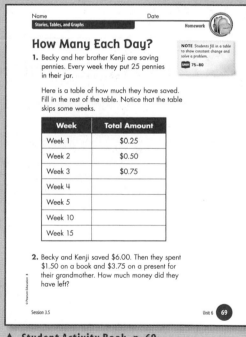

▲ **Student Activity Book, p. 69**

What Do the Graphs Show?

Math Focus Points

◆ Identifying points on a graph with corresponding values in a table and interpreting the numerical information in terms of the situation the graph represents

◆ Comparing situations by describing differences in their graphs

Today's Plan		Materials
1 ACTIVITY **Using Graphs to Compare,** *continued*	🕐 35 MIN 👥 PAIRS	• *Student Activity Book,* p. 53 (from Session 3.2) • *Student Activity Book,* pp. 61–63; 65–67 (from Sessions 3.4 and 3.5) • Colored pencils or crayons (optional)
2 DISCUSSION **What Do the Graphs Show?**	🕐 25 MIN 👥 CLASS	• T88; T89 🖥 • Chart paper* (2; optional)
3 SESSION FOLLOW-UP **Daily Practice and Homework**		• *Student Activity Book,* pp. 71–72 • *Student Math Handbook,* pp. 75–80, 81–86

*See *Materials to Prepare,* p. 77.

Ten-Minute Math

Guess My Rule Choose the rule "Factors of 48." Write four examples that fit this rule in a circle labeled "Follows My Rule." Allow students to suggest numbers that may or may not fit this rule and place them inside or outside the circle. Encourage students to name the rule in any way they can; for example, "All the numbers are factors of 48." or "They're all numbers you can count by to land on 48."

ACTIVITY

① Using Graphs to Compare, *continued*

35 MIN   PAIRS

Students complete *Student Activity Book* pages 61–63, and then work on *Student Activity Book* pages 65–67. They work in pairs but should complete their own student sheets. They can copy the values for Tovar from the table on *Student Activity Book* page 53.

Students plot points on a graph as they compare marble totals that increase at the same rate.

By plotting the points for two children on the same set of axes, students can compare what happens when one child starts with fewer marbles than another but accumulates marbles at a faster rate (Tovar and Gowen). They also compare what happens when two children start with a different number of marbles but accumulate marbles at the same rate (Tovar and Lazik).

Although Gowen begins with fewer marbles, he accumulates marbles at a greater rate, so his graph eventually intersects Tovar's. The graph on Completed Graphs for Tovar and Gowan (T88) shows that, although Lazik starts with fewer marbles than Tovar, the difference between them stays the same, so the points on the graph fall along two parallel lines.

Again, drawing light lines to connect the points for each Rhomaarian child, using two different colors, can be helpful in making the visual comparison between them and highlighting how one child's total marbles changes in relation to the other's total.

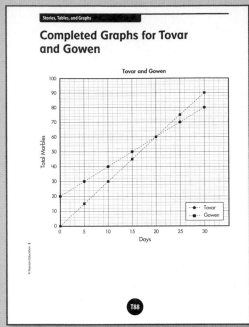

Stories, Tables, and Graphs

Completed Graphs for Tovar and Gowen

T88

▲ Transparencies, T88

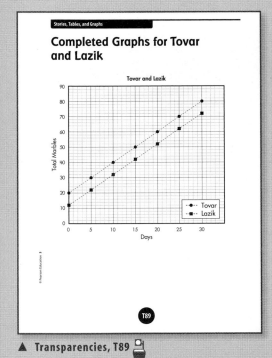

Stories, Tables, and Graphs

Completed Graphs for Tovar and Lazik

T89

▲ Transparencies, T89

ONGOING ASSESSMENT: Observing Students at Work

For complete details about observing this activity, see Session 3.5, pages 106–107.

DISCUSSION

2 What Do the Graphs Show?

25 MIN   CLASS

Math Focus Points for Discussion

◆ Identifying points on a graph with corresponding values in a table and interpreting the numerical information in terms of the situation the graph represents

◆ Comparing situations by describing differences in their graphs

Draw students' attention to the transparency of Completed Graphs for Tovar and Gowen (T88) or the large graph you made on chart paper for students to refer to during this discussion.

Who can say something about what the graphs of Tovar's and Gowen's marbles show?

As students respond, ask them where they see what they are describing on the graph. You can follow up with questions such as these:

Who has more Magic Marbles at the beginning of the month? Where can you see that on the graph? What about the middle of the month? What about the end of the month?

On which days does Tovar have more marbles than Gowen? During that time, what is happening—does Tovar get farther and farther ahead or is Gowen catching up? What shows you that on the graph?

On which days does Gowen have more marbles than Tovar? During that time, what is happening—does Gowen get farther and farther ahead or is Tovar catching up? What shows you that on the graph?

Who can show with their hands how Tovar's graph goes and how Gowen's graph goes?

Spend some time focusing on the point on the graph that is the same for Tovar and Gowen.

On what day do Tovar and Gowen have the same number of Magic Marbles? Where can you see that on the graph? What happens after that day?

Now show students the transparency of Completed Graphs for Tovar and Lazik (T89) or the large graphs you made on chart paper.

Ask the same kinds of questions about what the graphs show about Tovar and Lazik. After students describe what is happening on the graph, ask these questions:

What is happening as the month goes on? Does one of the children catch up to the other? How can you tell by looking at the graph? If Tovar and Lazik kept getting the same number of Magic Marbles every night for another 30 days and we continued our graphs for them, what would the graphs look like? Who can show with their hands how the graphs would look? ❶

SESSION FOLLOW-UP
Daily Practice and Homework

 Daily Practice: For ongoing review, have students complete *Student Activity Book* page 71.

 Homework: Students solve multiplication and division problems in story contexts on *Student Activity Book* page 72.

 Student Math Handbook: Students and families may use *Student Math Handbook* pages 75–80, 81–86 for reference and review. See pages 156–161 in the back of this unit.

Professional Development

❶ **Dialogue Box:** Using Graphs to Compare Situations with a Constant Rate of Change, p. 153

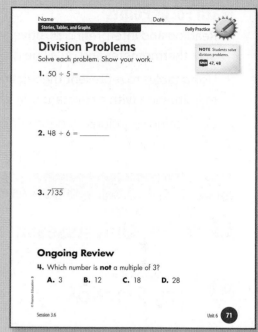

▲ **Student Activity Book, p. 71**

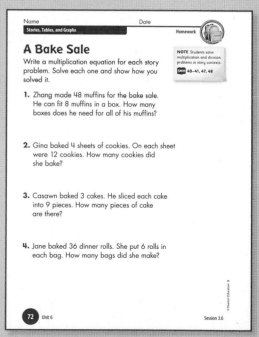

▲ **Student Activity Book, p. 72**

End-of-Unit Assessment

Math Focus Points

◆ Reading and interpreting positive and negative temperatures on a thermometer and on a line graph

◆ Using tables to represent the relationship between two quantities in a situation with a constant rate of change

◆ Comparing situations by describing differences in the tables that represent them

Today's Plan		Materials
ASSESSMENT ACTIVITY ❶ **End-of-Unit Assessment** ✔ 🕐 👤 **60 MIN** **INDIVIDUALS**		• M30–M36*
SESSION FOLLOW-UP ❷ **Daily Practice**		• *Student Activity Book,* p. 73 • *Student Math Handbook,* pp. 66–69, 70, 75–80, 81–86

*See *Materials to Prepare,* p. 77.

Ten-Minute Math

Guess My Rule   Choose the rule "Factors of 42." Write four examples that fit this rule in a circle labeled "Follows My Rule." Allow students to suggest numbers that may or may not fit this rule and place them inside or outside the circle. Encourage students to name the rule in any way they can; for example, "All the numbers are factors of 42" or "They're all numbers you can count by to land on 42."

ASSESSMENT ACTIVITY
End-of-Unit Assessment

60 MIN INDIVIDUALS

The End-of-Unit Assessment (M30–M36) consists of two problem sets. In Problem A, Temperature on Two Days, students read, interpret, and describe temperature graphs for a day in July and a day in December in Sydney, Australia. It addresses Benchmark 1: Interpret graphs of change over time, including both the meaning of points on the graph and how the graph shows that values are increasing, decreasing, or staying the same. Problem A also addresses Benchmark 2: Interpret temperature values (i.e., relate temperatures to seasons, to what outdoor clothing would be needed, and so on). In Problem B, Sophie's and Tom's Race, students create a table for a situation with a constant rate of change, in the context of running a certain number of miles each day, and to compare the two situations. It addresses Benchmark 3: Create a table of values for a situation with a constant rate of change and explain the values in the table in terms of the situation. Problem B also addresses Benchmark 4: Compare related situations of constant change by interpreting the graphs, tables, and sequences that represent those situations.

Distribute the End-of-Unit Assessment to students (M30–M36). Spend a few minutes introducing each of the problems to make sure that students understand each of the contexts and each of the tasks. Students then work individually on the End-of-Unit Assessment. Provide additional paper if some students need more room to answer questions.❶

Professional Development

❶ **Teacher Note:** End-of-Unit Assessment, p. 134

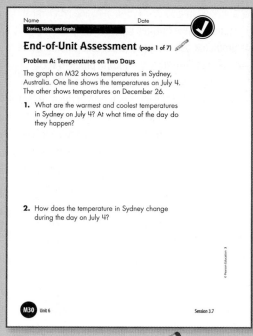

▲ Resource Masters, M30

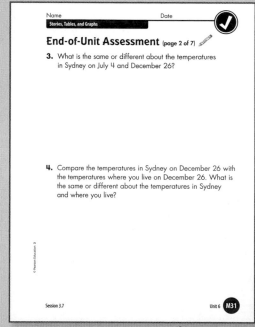

▲ Resource Masters, M31

Teaching Note

❷ **Introducing the Problems** You may decide to introduce these problems one at a time. If so, allow about 20 minutes for Problem A, and when most students have finished with the temperature problems, ask everyone to put that problem aside while you introduce the second problem set. Then those students who need more time on the temperature problems can return to them. You may also want to introduce the second problem set to small groups as they finish the first problem set. It is important that all students have the opportunity to clearly understand the new story context of the second problem and the task that each problem requires of them. This way, you are assessing their mathematical ideas rather than their reading skills or their experience with the context of running a race.

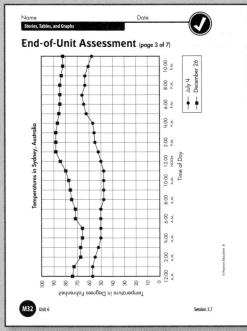

 Resource Masters, M32

ONGOING ASSESSMENT: Observing Students at Work

Students interpret and describe temperature graphs. They also create a table for a situation of constant change, answer questions about how the table represents the situation, and compare the two situations of constant change.

- **Can students identify the high and low temperatures and when they occurred?**

- **Can students interpret the visual features of a graph: high, low, increasing, decreasing?**

- **Can students describe and compare the overall shape of the lines that represent the two days?**

- **Can students relate the temperature values shown on the graph to their own experience of temperatures in December?**

- **Can students complete the table for two sequences in a situation of constant change accurately?**

- **Can students interpret what a row of the table represents in terms of the situation?**

- **Can students find the total number of miles for each racer for Day 14?**

- **Can students describe and compare how Tom's and Sophie's total miles increase over time?** Can they explain why Tom will not catch up to Sophie if they each continue running the same number of miles per day?

DIFFERENTIATION: Supporting the Range of Learners

Intervention Make sure that students correctly identify the line for July 4 when they answer Questions 1 and 2 in Problem A. Note for yourself any students who have difficulty making use of the key because this is a skill that they should develop. However, allow them to correct their mistake, if they at first began to describe the line for December 26, so that you can get good information to assess Benchmarks 1 and 2.

Intervention You may want to give out the pages of the problem one at a time so that students can focus on one page and do not become overwhelmed by seeing all the problems at once.❷ Keep in mind that students may need their table on End-of-Unit Assessment (M34) to work on subsequent problems.

 **Extension** Students who finish early can complete any remaining work on the student sheets in this investigation or work on the following problem:

Garon and Sujo live on Rhomaar. On day 30, Garon had 210 marbles and Sujo had 240 marbles. Each of them started with 30 marbles. How many marbles did Garon get each day? How many marbles did Sujo get each day? Show how you figured this out.

SESSION FOLLOW-UP

2 Daily Practice

 Daily Practice: For enrichment, have students complete *Student Activity Book* page 73.

 Student Math Handbook: Students and families may use *Student Math Handbook* pages 66–69, 70, 75–80, 81–86 for reference and review. See pages 156–161 in the back of this unit.

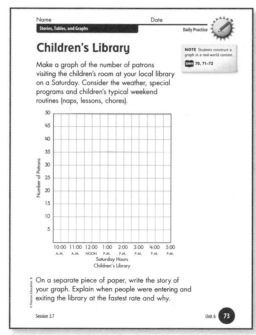

▲ **Student Activity Book, p. 73**

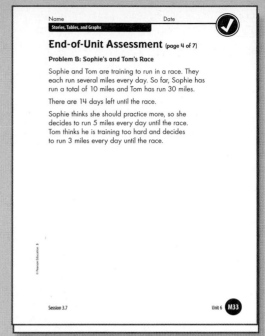

▲ **Resource Masters, M33–M34**

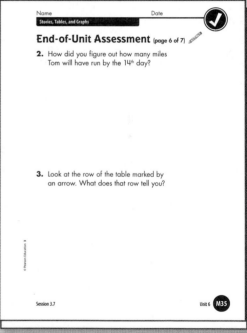

▲ **Resource Masters, M35–M36**

Using Line Graphs to Represent Change

In this unit, students use and interpret coordinate graphs that show how one quantity, such as temperature (in Investigation 1) or the number of marbles (in Investigation 3), changes over time.

Many of your students will be more experienced with graphs that show frequency than with graphs that show change over time. Graphs such as line plots or bar graphs show the frequency with which different values of one quantity occur. For example, this line plot shows the number of cavities of a group of children who visited a dentist in a particular week. It shows how many times each value (two cavities, three cavities, and so on) occurs.

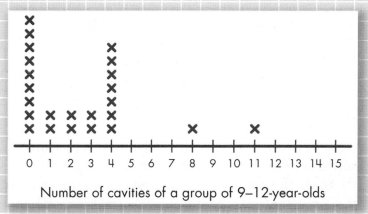

Number of cavities of a group of 9–12-year-olds

In this unit, students encounter a very different kind of graph. Line graphs show a relationship between two quantities; for example, temperature and time or number of marbles and time. When students first encounter these new kinds of situations in which they are relating change in one quantity to change in another, they may try to use what they know about bar graphs and line plots to represent them and may at first have difficulty understanding how one point on a graph can represent two related values.

Conventions of Line Graphs

When students learn to use a conventional representation, such as a line graph, aspects of the meaning of the representation that adults take for granted may not be obvious to students who have less experience with that representation. As students use line graphs to represent temperature in Investigation 1, help students with the conventions of this kind of graphing. Students will need time and experience to learn how a point on the graph represents a relationship between two variables. For example, a point on this graph shows a relationship between a date and a temperature.

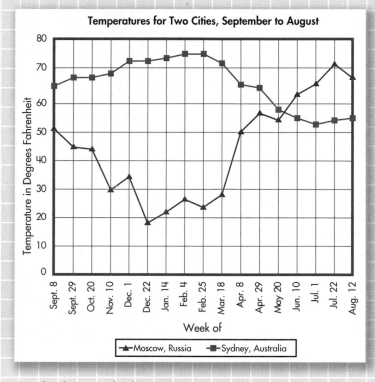

Temperatures for Two Cities, September to August

On this line graph, the temperature in Moscow on April 8 is 50 degrees. The point on the graph that represents this temperature is at the intersection of a line drawn perpendicular to the x-axis at April 8 with a line drawn perpendicular to the y-axis at 50°F. Even if these lines are not actually drawn on a graph, one imagines the intersection of such lines in order to read the information on the graph. It may seem natural to adults that a point can represent two values (e.g., a temperature of 50°F and a point in time, April 8), but students need experience learning to read this conventional representation. Students may use their fingers to trace the drawn or imagined lines from a point on the graph to the values on each axis.

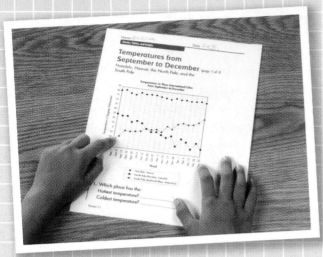

Students trace from the x-axis to a point on the graph to determine its value.

Sometimes students actually want to draw these lines (if they are not already part of the grid on the graph), but teachers' experience is that drawing such lines often makes the graph more difficult to read in the long run and that students gradually learn to read graphs themselves after tracing lines with their fingers for a short time. Students may also place rulers from a point on the graph to each axis at first to help them read the values for that point.

In Grade 3, students make graphs on axes that are already set up that so they do not need to choose which variable goes on which axis. There are conventions for establishing which axis of a graph and which column of a table are used for which variable. For example, in Investigation 3, the total number of marbles is dependent on the number of days that has passed; therefore, the total number of marbles is designated as the dependent variable and the number of days is the independent variable. The convention in creating tables and graphs is that values of the independent variable appear in the first column of the table and are graphed on the horizontal or *x*-axis. In the situations in this unit, the independent variable is time and the dependent variables are temperature (Investigation 1) and number of marbles (Investigation 3).

Line Graphs Show Both Values and How Those Values Are Changing

After the conventions of reading and creating line graphs have been established, focus on both how the graph shows values and how it shows change over time. One kind of information that the temperature graph shown on the previous page provides is particular temperatures on particular dates; for example, the temperature in Sydney was about 75 degrees on February 4.

But this graph also provides other important information—how the temperature is generally increasing, decreasing, or staying the same. An important focus of students' work is to learn how a line graph indicates change. In their work on temperature in Investigation 1, students learn about associating the shape of sections of a graph with general trends. For example, even though there are many fluctuations in temperature from Dec. 22 to July 22 in Moscow, with temperatures sometimes going up and sometimes going down from week to week, the general trend is an increase in temperature from the low on Dec. 22 to the high on July 22.

Students who are using line graphs for the first time may at first list each change in temperature as they describe the graph: "It went up and then up and then down and then up and then up and then up and then down." Ask questions that help focus on general trends ("In general, was the temperature increasing or decreasing or staying about the same from December to July?"), encourage students to use hand gestures to show how the temperature is changing, and discuss the differences in clothing and activities in various periods of time.

The graphs of temperature are examples of change that occurs at varying rates. From one week to the next week, temperature may increase or decrease, and that change may be gradual or rapid. In Investigation 3, students encounter a situation in which change takes place at a constant rate. The two situations provide an important contrast. See **Teacher Note:** Graphs of Situations with a Constant Rate of Change, page 130 for more information about the graphs in Investigation 3.

Assessment: A Summer Day in Cairo, Egypt

Problems 1, 2, and 3

Benchmark addressed:

Benchmark 1: Interpret graphs of change over time, including both the meaning of points on the graph and how the graph shows that values are increasing, decreasing, or staying the same.

In order to meet the benchmark, students' work should show that they can:

• Describe the overall changes in temperature from 6 A.M. to 10 P.M.;

• Write the suggested phrases on appropriate parts of the graph;

• Determine the highest (88° or 89°) and lowest (72° or 73°) temperatures.

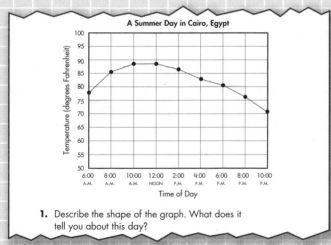

A Summer Day in Cairo, Egypt

Temperature (degrees Fahrenheit) vs. Time of Day

1. Describe the shape of the graph. What does it tell you about this day?

▲ **Resource Masters, M20**

2. On your graph, write the following above each part of the line where the temperature is:

Getting warmer   Getting cooler   Staying the same

3. What is the highest temperature on the graph? _____
   What is the lowest temperature? _____

▲ **Resource Masters, M21**

Meeting the Benchmark

Students who meet the benchmark show that they understand how temperature and times of the day are related by their descriptions for Problem 1 as in these examples.

It goes up and then starts dropping even lower then the start.
Its worm in the morning then it gets even hotter in the afternoon and then gets colder then the morning and afternoon.

Gina's Work

It is hottest at about 11:00 a.m.
It is collest at 10:00 p.m.
It is a teany tiny little bit cooler than it is hear about 5°F cooler

Nicholas's Work

It started out warm. Then it got warmer, and warmer. By the time you would be in bed it was cooler than the morning.

Gil's Work

There is 2 warm parts of the day and one hot part of the day. It seems that the warmer parts of the day is in the morning and night. The hot part of the day is around noon.

Nancy's Work

These student descriptions include phrases that make it clear that they are talking about temperature, not just that the graph goes "up" and "down." A few students may also notice that the rate at which the temperature increases is greater than the rate at which it decreases. For example, Benjamin wrote, "It is hot in the morning, gets hotter quickly, slowly cools down."

Students who meet the benchmark also demonstrate that they can read points on the graph by correctly determining the high and low temperatures and that they know how the graph shows change by placing the phrases on the graph approximately, as Nancy does.

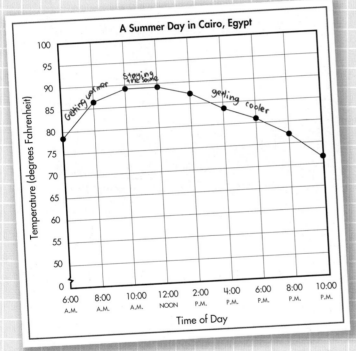

Nancy's Work

Some students write the phrases in every interval between points, as Nicholas does.

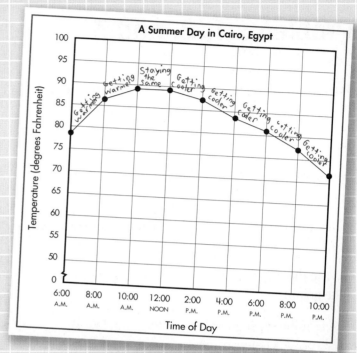

Nicholas's Work

Note that, because the temperature scale is shown in multiples of 5 and the dots on the graph are large, answers of 88° or 89° for the high temperature and 72° or 73° for the low temperature are acceptable. Third graders should be able to estimate within a degree by noticing where the point on the graph is relative to the temperature interval in which it occurs (e.g., "It's around halfway between 70° and 75°, so I think it's about 72°.").

Partially Meeting the Benchmark

Students who partially meet the benchmark show that they have some understanding of how the graph represents temperature. They are able to identify the high and low temperatures for the day, but they do not clearly describe the change over the day.

> it was a warm summer day like here it had some high timPretures it looked a howl lot like here

Murphy's Work

> It tells me about it is getting really hot. Then it went down to 73°

Jane's Work

Murphy knows that the graph shows warm temperatures but does not describe how the temperature increases and decreases. Jane seems to describe different points on the graph, but she does not describe the overall way the temperature increased and decreased during the day. Students' responses to Problem 2 provide additional evidence about whether they can fully interpret the graph. For example, Jane does place the phrases correctly on her graph, indicating the three sections as Nancy did above. However, Jane seems to focus on only individual points on her graph as she did in her description.

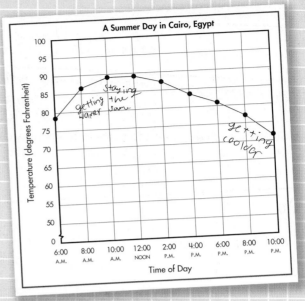

Jane's Work

Find out whether these students can elaborate on their description by asking questions such as these:

Where are the high temperatures you mentioned? What is happening during the rest of the day? If you were reporting the weather on the news, what would you tell people this day was like?

Not Meeting the Benchmark

Most students who do not meet the benchmark are able to identify the high and low temperatures from the graph, but are not able to use the graph to describe how the temperature changes over time. Many of these students describe the graph as a shape with no reference to how it represents temperature.

> It's like a curve. It gets high near the beggining

Arthur's Work

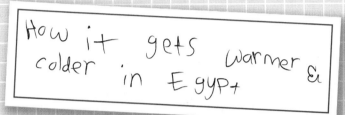

It looks like a rollercouster because it goes up then it goes down ↓.

Kelley's Work

Some students do make some reference to temperature but do not describe how it changes over time.

How it gets warmer & colder in Egypt

Bridget's Work

The shape looks like a hill! That it is summer.

Edwin's Work

As the unit continues, students will again work with line graphs in Investigation 3. Support them to use words and phrases that describe the change over time that the graph represents. All of the graphs in Investigation 3 represent an increase over time. Ask students periodically to contrast these graphs about the accumulation of marbles for a certain number of days at a constant rate with the class temperature graph—how are they the same and how are they different? The contrast between the irregular temperature graphs and the way the points fall in a straight line for the marble graphs can help students see how graphs represent different kinds of change. Also encourage students to use hand gestures to show what is happening over time, especially as they compare two children accumulating marbles at different rates.

Problems 4 and 5

Benchmark addressed:

Benchmark 2: Interpret temperature values (i.e., relate temperatures to seasons, to what outdoor clothing would be needed, and so on).

In order to meet the benchmark, students' work should show that they can:

- Relate temperature values shown on the graph to people's experience of temperatures in the 70s and 80s;

- Recognize that people experience temperatures close to 90° as hot;

- Recognize that the temperature varies during the day from hot to cooler but that, although the temperature goes down at night, it is still warm.

4. What kind of clothing might you wear if you were in Cairo on this day?

5. Compare this day in Cairo with a day where you live. Is there a month when you might have a day like this in your town?

▲ **Resource Masters, M21**

Meeting the Benchmark

Students who meet the benchmark show that they understand that this day is generally warm to hot and identify appropriate clothing for these temperatures. There is certainly variation in how people experience temperatures, so, for example, some students may suggest a sweater for 10 P.M. and others may think that a t-shirt and shorts would be comfortable. Accept responses that are reasonable.

Most students respond with one set of clothing.

> I might wear suntan lotion, Short, a hat, tanktop and a pair of sunglasses.

Kenji's Work

> I whold wear shorts and a tshirt and have 5 water jugs

Ines's Work

Some students describe clothing for different parts of the day.

> You might wear shorts and short shleves with sandles. At night you wear your summer pajams. With no blankets.

Deondra's Work

Note that some students also provide evidence in their responses to Problem 1 that they understand how these temperatures feel to people.

> The day starts off warm. Then later in the day, it get hoter as the day goes on. During the night, it get cooler, but not to cold.

Pilar's Work

Partially Meeting and Not Meeting the Benchmark

There may be students who are either unable to read the graph or unable to interpret that these temperatures feel warm to hot. It will be particularly important to involve these students as you continue to collect data for the class temperature graph. As you record temperatures, ask students to focus on the day's temperature, what season it is, what they are wearing, and how the outside temperature feels to them. Ask students these questions as they come in from recess:

How did it feel outside? Would you say that it's hot, warm, cool, or cold? Did you need a jacket? A hat? Mittens? What is the temperature today? What was it when we recorded it this week? How does it feel outside when it is in the [50s] as it is today?

Keep in mind that many students get hot and sweaty after being active at recess, no matter what the weather! However, students can talk about what it feels like when they first go outside and how that changes as they engage in active games or sports.

Use students' immediate experience with the outdoors to compare the current temperature with temperatures on the class graph.

Look at our temperatures this month so far. [Oscar] noticed that they're all in the [60s]. Are they like the temperatures last month? Do you remember the day last month when we walked to the river? Did that day feel warmer, colder, or the same as today?

Teacher Note

Repeating Patterns and Counting Numbers

Associating the counting numbers with the elements in a repeating pattern provides a context in which students can use familiar repeating patterns to investigate related number sequences.

In the repeating color pattern red-blue-green, red-blue-green, the unit of the pattern has three elements: red is the first element, blue is the second element, and green is the third element. Therefore, when a cube train that is built according to this pattern is numbered in sequence with the counting numbers, starting at 1, each multiple of 3 is associated with green.

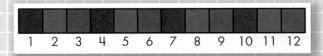

The multiples of 3 would be associated in this way with the third element in any repeating pattern with an ABC unit. For example, think about creating a repeating pattern with body movements and counting each movement as you do it. In the body movement pattern, slap knees–clap–tap shoulders, the third element (tap shoulders) always corresponds to a multiple of three.

As students investigate three-element repeating color patterns, they encounter three different "counting by 3" sequences. In the red-blue-green pattern, the greens fall on multiples of 3. The multiples of 3 are an anchor for students in understanding the red-blue-green pattern. After they have established that all greens fall on multiples of 3, they can use this information to figure out the colors associated with other numbers: the numbers associated with the blue cubes are the sequence 2, 5, 8, 11, . . . and the numbers associated with the red squares are the sequence 1, 4, 7, 10, . . .

When students have established that the last element in the pattern (green) always falls on a multiple of 3, and they have generated the number sequences associated with the blue cubes and the red cubes, they use this information to figure out numbers associated with particular cubes in the repeating pattern. For example, to find the color of the 25th cube in the red-blue-green sequence, students' methods may include: 1) putting two 12-cube trains together to get 24 and then seeing that cube 25 would be red; 2) counting by 1s and using the 12-cube train twice, then counting on one more; 3) reasoning that a 12-cube train ends with green, that two 12-cube trains have a total of 24 cubes and that the 24th cube is also green and will be followed by red; or 4) observing that 24 is green because it is a multiple of three (or counting by threes to reach 24) and knowing that red follows green.

Visualizing how the pattern works can become difficult as numbers get larger. Some students try to use the doubling that helped them find the color of the 25th cube (double 12 to get 24 and then add on one more cube) for numbers for which doubling does not work. Kim knows that the 25th cube is red. She reasons, "If you just add another 25 and get 50, it would still be red. So then count on three more cubes, and the 53rd is red, too."

Kim imagines that if she puts together two trains of 25, the 50th cube will also be red. However, 25 is not a multiple of 3, and does not end with a complete unit of red-blue-green. The 25th cube is red. Therefore, she cannot attach another 25-cube train that starts again with red. This breaks the pattern:

Most third graders will not completely sort out when doubling works and when it does not. Work on this idea is a focus in the Grade 4 Patterns, Functions, and Change unit, *Penny Jars and Plant Growth*.

Underlying the number sequences for each color in the pattern is an implicit function. Each green cube falls on a multiple of 3, so we can develop a rule that associates the sequence of green cubes with their numbers: the first green square is associated with 3, the second with 6, the third with 9, and so on. Although students do not make tables or write equations to describe these patterns in Investigation 2, they are developing rules to answer questions (e.g., what color is the 53rd cube in the pattern?) about the underlying functional relationship that is represented in the following table:

Number of green cubes	Position in red-blue-green sequence
1 (first green cube)	3
2 (second green cube)	6
3 (third green cube)	9
4 (fourth green cube)	12
5 (fifth green cube)	15
6 (sixth green cube)	18

Some students may say, "To find the number for the 10th green cube, multiply 10 by 3." This work on developing a rule that relates the two variables. becomes more explicit in Investigation 3. See **Algebra Connections in This Unit,** page 16, for more information about linear functions.

Teacher Note

Students' Representations of Change

In Investigation 3, students are introduced to a fantasy situation about a constant rate of change. As students investigate this situation, they learn how two variables are related. In order to describe this relationship, students think through how to take into account a starting amount and a constant rate of change. This relationship is an example of a linear function. See **Algebra Connections in This Unit,** page 16, for more information.

In the activity in Session 3.1, students create their own representations of the accumulation of Magic Marbles by one child. Given the number of marbles saved from the year before and the number of marbles received every night, they find a way to show the accumulation of the marbles over 30 days. In this way, students make sense of the important elements in this situation for themselves and think through how these elements are related (e.g., how addition and multiplication come into play). As they work on their representations, you can assess whether students understand the story; whether they grasp the mathematical relationships among the starting amount, rate of change, and total number of marbles, and what knowledge of representations they draw on.

Some students create sequences of numbers, showing the increase in total number of marbles each day. For example, Kelley and Dwayne made a chart that looked like this for Zupin (these are the first three rows of their chart):

2	2	2	4	2	6	2	8
2	10	2	12	2	14	2	16
2	18	2	20	2	22	2	24

Kelley and Dwayne's Work

Dwayne explained, "We're counting 2 each night, and then we'll add 60."

Like Kelley and Dwayne, Jung does not include the starting amount until the end. She writes the following:

Starts with 60

1. O O
2. O O
3. O O
4. O O
5. O O
. . .
. . .

After she finishes her list, she counts all the circles and then adds 60.

Many students make lists like Gil's.

1. 62
2. 64
3. 66
4. 68
5. 70
.
.
.

Gil's representation clearly shows the total number of marbles each day, as does one by Nicholas and Ines. Here is the first row of their representation:

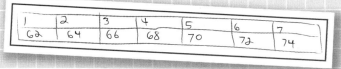

1	2	3	4	5	6	7
62	64	66	68	70	72	74

Nicholas and Ines's Work

Notice that Nicholas and Ines made seven days in each row, as on a calendar.

Students also create various kinds of tables. Elena created a table that shows how multiplication is related to the accumulating total.

Number of marbles Each Night		Night	Total Marbles
2	×	1	2
2	×	2	4
2	×	3	6
2	×	4	8

Elena's Work

Elena explained, "I'm figuring the number of marbles each night, and this [points to the first column] times this [points to the second column] equals this [points to the third column]." Her table does not yet take into account the leftover marbles; she may be planning to add them at the end as Kelley, Dwayne, and Jung do.

Her partner, Kathryn, wanted to include the leftover marbles from the beginning. Her table looked like this:

Left Over	Number of marbles Each Night	Total
60	2	62
	2	64
	2	66
	2	68

Kathryn's Work

Students can benefit from comparing representations. What does each show clearly? What does each not show? Where can you see the starting amount in each? The rate of change? The total number of marbles after 30 days? Does the representation show the number of marbles for any day?

Teacher Note

Using and Interpreting Tables

In Grade 2, students began to use tables to represent the relationship between two variables. Beginning in Session 3.2 of this unit, students use tables to record data about how the number of marbles each Rhomaarian child has changes over the course of 30 days.

Many third graders should already be familiar with tables. However, if some of your students are not experienced with tables, this representation can seem full of vertical and horizontal lines and words and numbers and may not, at first, make sense to them. Only through moving back and forth between the numbers in the table and the situation these numbers represent do students develop an understanding of what information is provided in a table and how the parts of the table are related.

As you discuss the information in the tables with your students, it is useful to use the words *row* (to mean a horizontal slice of the table) and *column* (to mean a vertical slice of the table). When you use these words, indicate with gestures to what part of the table you are referring. As you model the correct use of these words in context, students learn their meaning which, in turn, allows them to talk more clearly about the information in a table.

In this unit, students first use tables in which one variable increases by 1s, as in this table for Franick's marbles.

Day	Franick
Beginning	30
1	33
2	36
3	39
4	42

Students have used tables like the one above in Grade 2, in which the first column of the table always showed an increase of one. As this unit continues, students use tables in which not every value is shown in the first column. This table shows Franick's total marbles for every five days:

Day	Franick
Beginning	30
5	45
10	60
15	75
20	90

There are two ideas that are important here: the meaning of each row and how the numbers change from row to row. For example, the row with the arrows shows that after ten days, Franick had 60 marbles; the next row shows that after 15 days, Franick had 75 marbles. What accounts for the change in the values between these two rows? Five more days have passed (Days 11, 12, 13, 14, 15), and Franick has accumulated 15 more marbles (60 + 15 = 75). Franick receives three marbles each day, so she receives 15 marbles every five days (3 marbles per day × 5 days = 15 marbles). When students understand how to interpret tables that show the number of marbles after every five days, they can use them to describe and compare how the number of marbles is changing. See **Dialogue Box:** Why Are There Five 2s?, page 150. Making graphs that are based on these tables, in which every fifth day is shown, allows students to create a graph that represents the relationship between the two variables (number of days, total number of marbles) without having to plot so many points.

One of the key issues in learning about tables is understanding what the information in each column and in each row means. Students in the elementary grades often find the patterns they see in a *column* of a table compelling. For example, in the table for Zupin's marbles (Zupin starts with 60 marbles and gets two marbles each day), they notice that the numbers in the first column (number of days) increase by 5, while the numbers in the second column (total number of marbles) increase by 10.

Day	Zupin
Beginning	60
5	70
10	80
15	90
20	100

Students' attention is likely to be captured by these patterns. They may focus on extending the number pattern, but can lose their sense of what the numbers show about the situation, in this case, that the number of marbles increase by 10 every five days.

Although the number patterns in a column of a table carry important information, it is also crucial for students to focus on the relationship of numbers in each row of the table because it is the row that shows the relationship between the two variables. You can point to a row of the table and ask, "Who can say a sentence about this row of the table? What information do the numbers in this row give us about Zupin?" Looking at the relationship between the numbers in the columns is particularly important as students develop rules that capture the relationship between the two variables (see Sessions 3.3 and 3.4). If students look only at each column separately, they may be able to say, "It goes up by ten each time," but they may not be able to develop and articulate a generalization about the relationship, such as, "The total number of marbles is two times the number of days plus 60," or explain how this rule relates to the situation. As you work with your students, emphasize the meaning of individual rows in the table in order to lay a foundation for describing the relationship between the variables.

Teacher Note

Graphs of Situations with a Constant Rate of Change

Throughout this unit, students use and interpret graphs plotted on a coordinate grid to show how the values of one quantity change in relationship to the values of another. In Investigation 1, the graphs show temperature change over time. Students learn how points on these graphs represent the temperature for a particular date and how the shape of the line represents the change in temperature—whether it is decreasing, increasing, or staying the same. See **Teacher Note:** Using Line Graphs to Represent Change, page 117.

In Investigation 3, students notice that the points on their graphs of marble accumulation always fall in straight lines. Unlike the graphs of temperature, these graphs represent a situation with a constant rate of change. As one quantity changes by a certain amount, the other quantity always changes by a corresponding amount; for example, in the graph of Tovar's marbles, as the number of days increases by one, the total number of marbles increases by two.

This is true whether the number of days is increasing from 1 to 2 or from 14 to 15 or from 29 to 30. For every horizontal change of one, there is a vertical change of two, the slope or steepness of the graph is the same at any point, and the points on the resulting graph fall in a straight line.

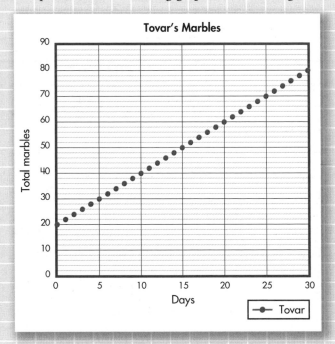

Graphs are particularly useful when comparing two different change situations. In Investigation 1, students compared temperature trends in different locations. The marble comparisons in Investigation 3 highlight the two components of situations with a constant rate of change—the starting amount and the rate of change. The three comparison situations that students encounter follow.

One child starts with fewer marbles than another but accrues marbles at a faster rate, represented by graphs that cross each other.

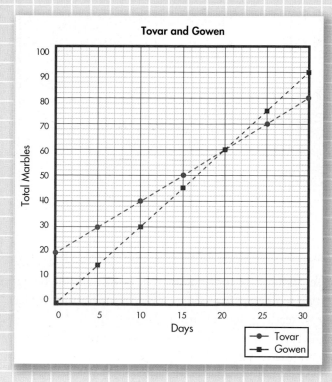

Two children start with the same number of marbles but accrue marbles at different rates, represented by graphs that start at the same point and then get farther and farther apart.

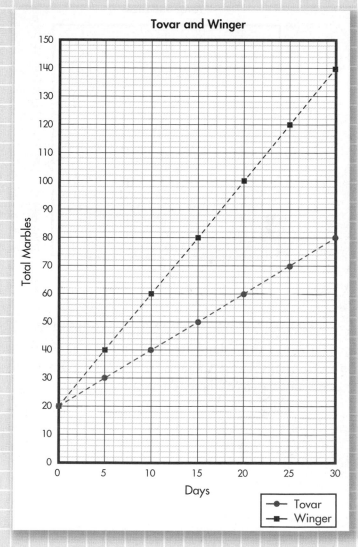

Note that the light lines connecting the points do not represent values. They are used here as an aid to show how each child's total marbles increases.

Two children start with different numbers of marbles, but accrue marbles at the same rate, represented by graphs that are parallel.

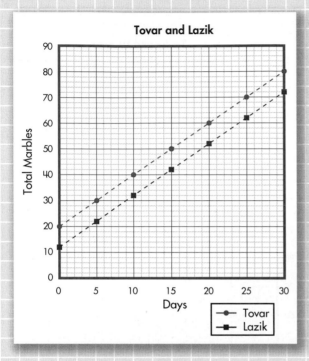

See **Dialogue Box:** Using Graphs to Compare Situations with a Constant Rate of Change, page 153, for examples of students' discussions of these comparisons.

Discrete and Continuous Change

The marble data are of a different type than the temperature data in another way as well. The temperature data are continuous, and the marble data are discrete. As temperature changes, from 75° to 80° between noon and 2 P.M., as shown on this graph, it must pass through all the values from 75° to 80°.

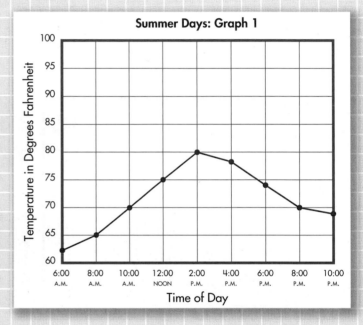

These changes are continuous; that is, in the time between any two temperature readings, every temperature between the two readings has occurred. At some time, the temperature was exactly 76.5°F; at some other time, the temperature was exactly 79.75°F or any other temperature value that falls between 75°F and 80°F. Such continuous change is shown by the line on the graph between the two temperatures. The line on this graph has a mathematical meaning. It shows that the temperature passes through all the values from 75°F to 80°F. However, there is a way in which this line is not precise. We graph the actual temperature data we have—in this case, the temperatures at noon and 2 P.M. Then we connect these data points to show how the temperature changed. However, because we do not know exactly when the temperature was 76°F or 79°F, the lines between the data points that represent actual temperature readings do not show completely accurate information. This inaccuracy is true of all line graphs to some extent. The more frequent the data readings and the more actual data points on the graph, the more accurate the shape of the line will be.

The marble data are discrete data: only certain values can occur. For example, Bolar has 5 marbles on Day 1 and 10 marbles on Day 2. However, there is no time when he has 7 marbles or 8.5 marbles, and there are no data for Day 1.5. Marbles, unlike temperature, are discrete objects and can have the values of only the counting numbers 1, 2, 3, 4, . . . (or an absence of any marbles can be represented as zero). Further, in this case, the children get marbles in bunches, so for each child only certain counting numbers occur as values for that child's total marbles. Similarly, the days occur as only whole numbers.

Although only certain points on the marble graphs have actual values in this discrete situation, it is often convenient to sketch a line between the points to highlight the trend of the changes shown on the graph. Unlike graphs of continuous data, all the points on this line do not represent actual values or estimates of actual values. However, it can help students see the constant rate of change and compare different situations of constant rate of change. For example, adding lines to the graph of Tovar's and Gowen's marbles

shown on page 131 helps the eye see the comparison more clearly. Without the lines drawn in, it can be difficult for students to distinguish which points represent Tovar's marbles and which points represent Gowen's marbles:

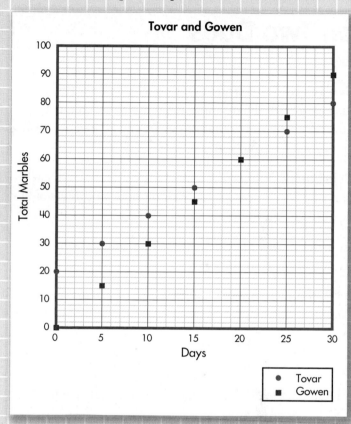

Students in Grade 3 need not be concerned with the subtle differences in the meaning of lines discussed in this Teacher Note. It is important for you to understand these issues as a teacher. Your students can use lines on the graph to help them see the overall patterns of change in both the temperature and the marble situations.

Note that throughout this unit, the phrase "situation of constant change" is used to designate a situation in which two variables are related by a constant rate of change. That is, for a certain amount of change in the value of one variable, there is always a certain amount of change in the value of the other variable (e.g., if the number of days increases by 1, the total number of marbles increases by 2).

End-of-Unit Assessment

Problem A: Temperatures on Two Days

Benchmarks addressed:

Benchmark 1: Interpret graphs of change over time, including both the meaning of points on the graph and how the graph shows that values are increasing, decreasing, or staying the same.

Benchmark 2: Interpret temperature values (i.e., relate temperatures to seasons, to what outdoor clothing would be needed, and so on).

In order to meet the benchmarks, students' work should show that they can:

- Determine which line on the graph represents the temperatures for July 4;

- Determine the highest and lowest temperatures for July 4 and when they occur;

- Describe the overall changes in temperature from 12 A.M. to 10 P.M. for July 4;

- Compare the temperatures for the two different dates, both in terms of temperature values and the change over the time period shown on the graph;

- Relate temperature values shown on the graph to their own experience of temperatures in the high 60s to the high 80s.

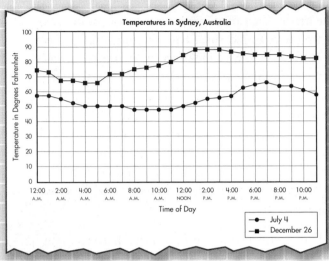

▲ Resource Masters, M32

Meeting the Benchmarks

Students who meet the benchmarks are able to identify the highest and lowest temperatures and when they occur: a response between 65°F and 67°F at 7:00 P.M. is reasonable for the highest temperature, and one between 47°F and 49°F at between 8:00 and 11:00 A.M. is reasonable for the lowest temperature. Some students may choose just one of the times (e.g., 10:00 A.M.) for the lowest temperature.

They describe how the temperature on July 4 decreases over the course of the morning, rises through the afternoon and early evening, and then decreases somewhat in the later evening. Oscar and Keisha have complete responses.

2. How does the temperature in Sydney change during the day on July 4?

It goes from 59° and get colder as the morning passes. As the afternoon comes it gets hotter and as the day passes it gets a little bit cooler.

Oscar's Work

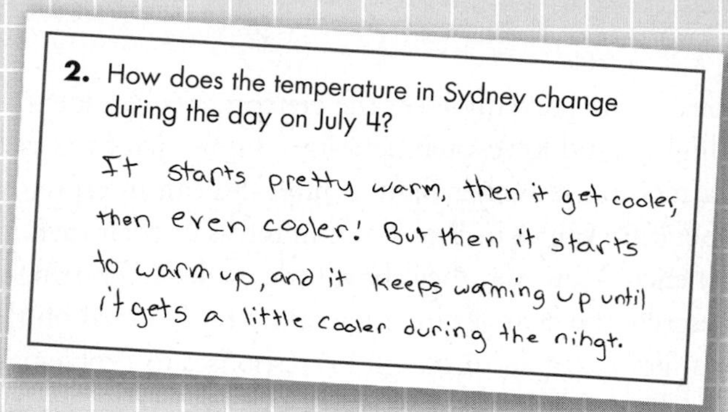

2. How does the temperature in Sydney change during the day on July 4?

It starts pretty warm, then it get cooler, then even cooler! But then it starts to warm up, and it keeps warming up until it gets a little cooler during the nihgt.

Keisha's Work

Students who meet the benchmarks are also able to compare the temperature in Sydney on July 4 with the temperature on December 26. Most students note that the temperature on December 26 is warmer overall. Many students also describe either similarities or differences in the temperature changes. Some students notice that the graphs have somewhat the same shape: first temperatures decrease somewhat, then they rise, and then they fall slightly. Although these changes are not matched exactly by time of day, there is a similarity in the sequence of changes. Other students notice some of the differences in the changes. Here are some examples of responses to Problem 3:

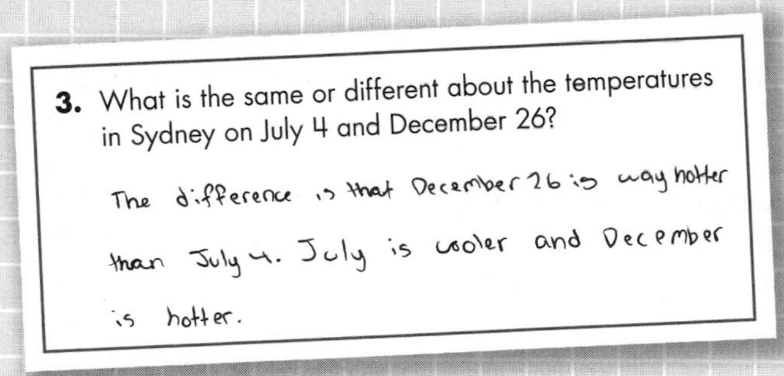

3. What is the same or different about the temperatures in Sydney on July 4 and December 26?

The difference is that December 26 is way hotter than July 4. July is cooler and December is hotter.

Oscar's Work

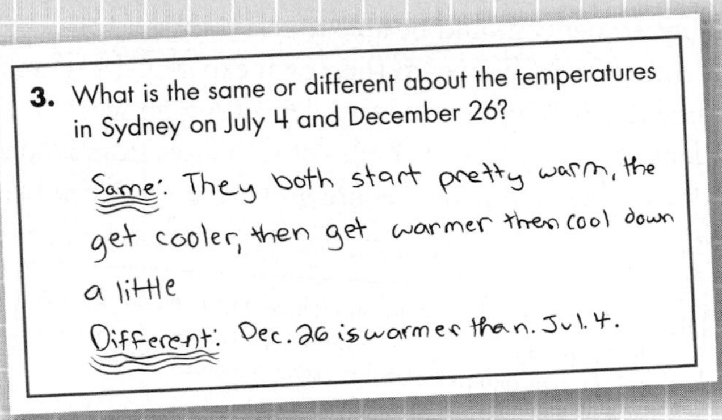

3. What is the same or different about the temperatures in Sydney on July 4 and December 26?

Same: They both start pretty warm, the get cooler, then get warmer then cool down a little

Different: Dec. 26 is warmer than. Jul. 4.

Keisha's Work

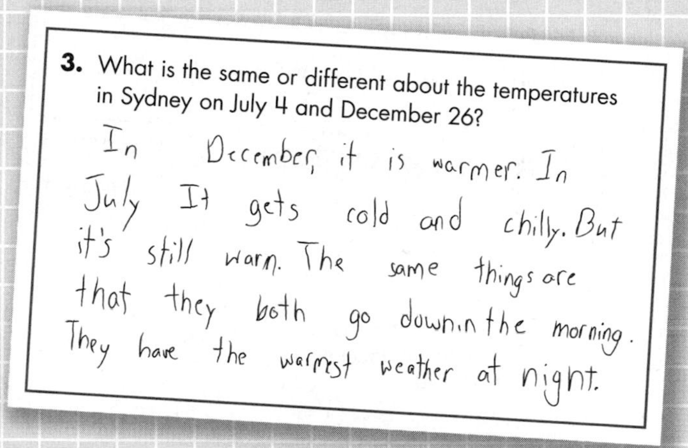

3. What is the same or different about the temperatures in Sydney on July 4 and December 26?

In December, it is warmer. In July It gets cold and chilly. But it's still warn. The same things are that they both go down in the morning. They have the warmest weather at night.

Elena's Work

Although students can choose somewhat different aspects of the graphs to write about in Problems 2 and 3, the combination of their responses to the first three questions should indicate that they can read, interpret, and compare the graphs and that they can both interpret the meaning of individual points on the graph and describe how the graph shows changes in temperature.

Finally, students should be able to relate temperatures on December 26 in Sydney to their own experiences. These experiences will, of course, vary depending on where your students live. Here are examples of responses from students who live where temperatures are quite cold in December:

> **4.** Compare the temperatures in Sydney on December 26 with the temperatures where you live on December 26. What is the same or different about the temperatures in Sydney and where you live?
>
> The temperature where I live is way colder. In Sydney it's so much warmer than here where I live. In December it's in the 20°s or the 30°s!

Chiang's Work

> **4.** Compare the temperatures in Sydney on December 26 with the temperatures where you live on December 26. What is the same or different about the temperatures in Sydney and where you live?
>
> Our temperratue is ~~way~~ colder. theirs is alot warmer and nicer. Ours is alot colder and darker. their winter is like our summer. I wish our winter was the same temperature as their winter.

Elena's Work

See Session 3.7 for information about students who describe the December 26 data instead of the July 4 data for Problems 1 and 2. If they did not respond correctly to this during the assessment session, focus on whether their descriptions of the December 26 data along with the other work on this problem do meet the benchmarks for this unit. Make a note that these students should work on interpreting the use of different symbols or colors used to distinguish different data sets on a graph.

Partially Meeting the Benchmarks

Students who partially meet the benchmarks can identify the highest and lowest temperatures, know that Sydney is warmer in December than in July, and can interpret temperature values in Problem 4 in terms of their own experience. However, they show little evidence of being able to describe the changes in temperature represented on the graph. For example, although his responses to Problems 1, 3, and 4 are good, Adam responds to Problem 2 as follows:

> **2.** How does the temperature in Sydney change during the day on July 4?
>
> It alwase incrses and decrses and sometimes stays the same.

Adam's Work

Overall, there is not enough evidence in what Adam writes that he can describe how the graph shows change over time. You may want to ask students like this to elaborate on their answers. Asking them some specific questions and having them show you what they mean by pointing to the graph can provide additional evidence of their understanding.

Another example is Philip's work. Like Adam, he writes good answers to Problems 1, 3, and 4, but he writes the following for Problem 2:

> **2.** How does the temperature in Sydney change during the day on July 4?
>
> It changes by like going up and down when it is at 65° the temertur goes down.

Philip's Work

Philip shows here, as on the other questions, that he can read points on a graph and has some understanding of how the graph shows change ("at 65° the tempertur goes down"), but he does not describe the overall change for the time period shown on the graph. In his response to Problem 3, he writes that December is warmer than July, but also does not describe how either of the graphs show change. Therefore, taking all his responses together, he partially meets the benchmarks.

Not Meeting the Benchmarks

Students who do not meet the benchmarks often respond correctly to Problems 1 and 4, showing that they have some skills reading a graph. However, they are not able to describe the changes in temperature shown by the graph. Some students, like Kathryn, try to pay attention to each fluctuation of the graph, often getting lost in all the separate changes, and do not describe any general trends of increasing, decreasing, or staying the same.

> **2.** How does the temperature in Sydney change during the day on July 4?
>
> It warm then cooler then cooler then warmer then warmer then cooler

Kathryn's Work

Other students, Benjamin, for example, describe the change in vague terms.

> **2.** How does the temperature in Sydney change during the day on July 4?
>
> it gets hoter and colder each day.

Benjamin's Work

Finally, Beatriz describes the graph only as a shape, not as a representation of temperature.

> **2.** How does the temperature in Sydney change during the day on July 4?
>
> It only goes like a hill it goes dwn then flat then up then flat

Beatriz's Work

These students can benefit from participating fully in ongoing discussions of the class temperature graph, relating their own experience of seasonal change to what the graph is showing. You may want to ask these students to be responsible for finding out the temperature each week and to record it on the class graph. You may also want to have informal discussions with them, perhaps when they come in each morning, about what the graph shows so far and how the temperature may change in the coming weeks.

Problem B: Sophie's and Tom's Race

Benchmarks addressed:

Benchmark 3: Create a table of values for a situation with a constant rate of change and explain the values in the table in terms of the situation.

Benchmark 4: Compare related situations of constant change by interpreting the graphs, tables, and sequences that represent those situations.

In order to meet the benchmarks, students' work should show that they can:

- Complete the table accurately;

- Determine how many miles Tom and Sophie will have run by Day 14 and explain how they figured this out;

- Explain that the numbers in the marked row show that by Day 6, Sophie had run 40 miles and Tom had run 48 miles;

- Compare how Tom's and Sophie's total miles change over time and explain why Tom will not catch up to Sophie in total miles if they each continue to run the same number of miles per day.

Name _____ Date _____

Stories, Tables, and Graphs

End-of-Unit Assessment (page 4 of 7)

Problem B: Sophie's and Tom's Race

Sophie and Tom are training to run in a race. They each run several miles every day. So far, Sophie has run a total of 10 miles and Tom has run 30 miles.

There are 14 days left until the race.

Sophie thinks she should practice more, so she decides to run 5 miles every day until the race. Tom thinks he is training too hard and decides to run 3 miles every day until the race.

▲ **Resource Masters, M33**

Meeting the Benchmarks

Students who meet the benchmarks fill in the table correctly, calculate the number of miles for the 14th day correctly, and can explain their calculation. For example, here is Kenji's work:

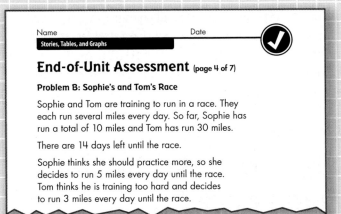

Days	Total Number of Miles	
	Sophie	Tom
So far	10	30
1	15	33
2	20	36
3	25	39
4	30	42
5	35	45
→ 6	40	48
7	45	51
8	50	54
9	55	57
10	60	60

b. There are four more days until the race. How many miles will Sophie and Tom have run by the 14th day?

14	80	72

2. How did you figure out how many miles Tom will have run by the 14th day?

I counted by threes four times to get to my Anser.

Kenji's Work

Students generally use one of two methods to find the number of miles run by Day 14. Some, like Kenji on page 138, multiply the number of miles per day by four and add the product to the total number of miles for Day 10. Others count up by five for Sophie and by three for Tom, either mentally or on paper as Jung does.

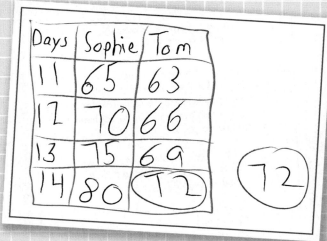

Jung's Work

Students interpret Problem 3 in different ways. Some students explain that the row of the table marked with an arrow provides the information that by Day 6, Sophie had run a total of 40 miles and Tom had run 48 miles:

> **3.** Look at the row of the table marked by an arrow. What does that row tell you?
>
> It tells me that on day 6 Sophie has ran 40 miles and Tom has ran 48.

Kenji's Work

Other students describe how the totals compare on Day 6 and how they are changing relative to each other.

> **3.** Look at the row of the table marked by an arrow. What does that row tell you?
>
> They are getting closer. Sophie has 40 and Tom has 48 (the day before they were 10 apart).

Nicholas's Work

> **3.** Look at the row of the table marked by an arrow. What does that row tell you?
>
> It tells me that thire finely in the 40's. there both in the 40's. Thats the first tim there like that on this table.

Gina's Work

> **3.** Look at the row of the table marked by an arrow. What does that row tell you?
>
> It tells me that sophies is behind but, she is cathing up by 2 every day.

Denzel's Work

All of these responses provide evidence that students understand how the table represents the situation.

Finally, students who meet the benchmark can compare how Sophie's and Tom's total miles change over time. They describe how Sophie started with fewer total miles but caught up and eventually surpassed Tom's total because she is adding on miles at a faster rate (five miles per day compared with Tom's three miles per day). Students should also understand that if they each continue practicing at the same rate, Tom's total will not catch up to Sophie's. In other words, these students can use and interpret the table to describe the situation as a whole. Use a combination of students' responses to Problems 4 and 5 to assess their understanding of how these two situations of constant change compare. Sometimes one response is more complete than the other, but between the two responses, the important elements of the situation are described. Here are examples of responses that meet the benchmarks:

4. How did Tom and Sophie compare at the beginning? How did they compare at the end? Why did this happen?

Tom started with more in the beginning and Sophie ended up with more.

5. On the day of the race, it rained. The race was rescheduled for 2 weeks later. If Sophie and Tom keep practicing at the same rate for 2 more weeks, will Tom ever catch up to Sophie in total miles? How do you know?

Because Tom runs 3 miles every 1 day. Sophie runs 5 miles every 1 day. So they will end up being different.

Zhang's Work

4. How did Tom and Sophie compare at the beginning? How did they compare at the end? Why did this happen?

No. Sophie had the lead after 14 days so, Tom will never catch up because he runs three miles every day and Sophie runs 5 miles every day.

5. On the day of the race, it rained. The race was rescheduled for 2 weeks later. If Sophie and Tom keep practicing at the same rate for 2 more weeks, will Tom ever catch up to Sophie in total miles? How do you know?

At the beginning, Tom was ahead by 20, and at the end behind by 8.

when they tied at 60 Tom kept running 3 miles, while sophie ran 5.

Tom 60 +3 63 +3 66 . . .

Sophie 60 +5 65 +5 70 . . .

No because Sophie is ahead and she is going 2 more miles then tom.

Jane's Work

Partially Meeting the Benchmarks

Some students make minor calculation errors but answer all of the other questions correctly. For example, if one mistake is made in the table when counting by 3s, all the other entries and answers to subsequent problems may be incorrect because they are based on that initial mistake. For example, Pilar writes 41 instead of 51 for Day 7 but correctly increases the total by three for each subsequent day and for Day 14.

Days	Total Number of Miles	
	Sophie	Tom
So far	10	30
1	15	33
2	20	36
3	25	39
4	30	42
5	35	45
6	40	48
7	45	41
8	50	49
9	55	47
10	60	50

b. There are four more days until the race. How many miles will Sophie and Tom have run by the 14th day?

14	80	62

Pilar's Work

In cases like this, you can see whether the student understood the central ideas being assessed by these benchmarks by looking at their responses after the mistake and their answers to Problems 2 through 5. Ask students to review their papers and find their errors. If these students often make these kinds of mistakes, talk with them about how to double-check their work and continue working with them to help them incorporate strategies for double-checking into their work.

Other students who partially meet the benchmarks complete the table correctly and answer Problems 2 and 3 correctly but are not able to answer Problems 4 and 5. These students seem to have a grasp of how the table represents the situation and can interpret individual values in the table. However, they are not yet able to see the table as a whole and use it to visualize how Sophie's and Tom's total miles change over time in relation to each other. These students meet Benchmark 3, but not Benchmark 4. They may simply state that Tom started out with a higher total and ended up with a lower total, but their explanations do not include anything about comparing Sophie's miles per day with Tom's.

4. How did Tom and Sophie compare at the beginning? How did they compare at the end? Why did this happen?

In the begining they were 20 apart and at the end their 10 apart.

I think it happened because they were Far apart in the begining, then they met they kept getting farther but Not as far as in the begining.

5. On the day of the race, it rained. The race was rescheduled for 2 weeks later. If Sophie and Tom keep practicing at the same rate for 2 more weeks, will Tom ever catch up to Sophie in total miles? How do you know?

I think the Probably wont Meet because they Met Now their getting farther apart.

Gil's Work

Other students try to actually calculate the number of miles Tom and Sophie will each add on over the next 14 days, but, whether their calculations are correct or incorrect, they still do not include in their responses to Problems 4 and 5 an explanation that focuses on Sophie's higher rate of miles per day.

Not Meeting the Benchmarks

Students who do not meet either of the benchmarks do not have adequate responses to almost all of the problems. Even if they fill out the table correctly, their explanation in Problem 3 does not provide evidence that they understand how the table represents the situation. Inadequate responses for Problems 4 and 5 are explained above.

If you have students who need more experience interpreting tables, find opportunities to make quick tables on the board that represent a constant ratio and are related to students' experiences. Ask questions that invite students to interpret the values in the tables. For example, pose these questions: "If there are eight weeks of school left, how many days are left? How many days in one week? Two weeks? Three weeks?" You can use any multiplication situation that involves equal groups in this way; for example, if there are 25 students in each class, how many students in five classes? In ten classes?

Total number of weeks	Total number of days
1	7
2	14
3	21
4	28
5	35

Number of classes	Total number of students
1	25
2	50
3	75
4	100
5	125

You can also use the Penny Jar situation that students worked with in Grade 2 and will work with again in Grade 4 to help students use tables to compare different situations of constant change. Here is a sample problem:

Kim has 30 pennies in her jar. She decides to save 2 pennies a day for 20 days.

Keith has 20 pennies in his jar. He decides to save 5 pennies a day for 20 days.

Make a table that shows how Kim's total pennies and Keith's total pennies change each day.

Ask students to describe and compare how the total number of pennies changes over time, using questions similar to those in Investigation 3 of this unit.

"The Shape Is Kind of Slanted"

In Session 1.2, students are discussing the shape of the graphs for the North Pole, South Pole, and Honolulu, Hawaii.

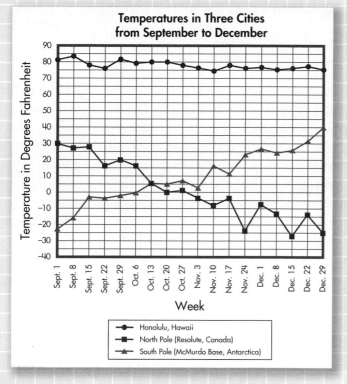

Teacher: Let's look at the North Pole graph. Can someone show me with your hand what the graph looks like?

Arthur: It goes down, and then it goes up and starts getting a little jagged.

Chiang: I think it's like this. [Chiang holds her hand diagonally, slanting down and to her right.]

Cameron: It's a diagonal going down. [shows with his arm]

Teacher: How is the temperature changing?

Chiang: It's getting colder.

Elena: The shape is kind of slanted.

Edwin: The temperature drops down about every week, it gets colder and colder. And sometimes it gets slightly warmer.

Teacher: Let's pretend that my arm shows the graph of the North Pole. [holds arm so that, when facing the class, it is imitating the shape of the North Pole line graph with fingertips at the highest temperature] What temperature would be at the tips of my fingers?

Edwin: 28 degrees!

Beatriz: That would be September 1st.

Teacher: How would you draw a line for the South Pole that shows the general temperature trend from September to December?

Keith comes up to the board and draws this line:

Cameron: But temperature keeps changing. There are lots of spikes.

Kenji: I agree with Keith that overall it is going higher. The line has jags and goes down sometimes. But it goes farther up than it is going down. It goes down a little and more up.

Teacher: Overall would you say that it is getting warmer or colder?

Oscar: A little of both, but mostly hotter.

Teacher: If we look back at the diagonal line that Keith drew, what does it show us?

Zhang: It tells us how it changes. It's diagonal. Like the North Pole, but that one goes down diagonally.

Chris: The South Pole line tells us that the temperature goes up.

Kelley: It's getting warmer.

Teacher: What are some other words or phrases you can say for the diagonal up?

Beatriz: Could you say that it's dropping up? Like you say dropping down?

Elena: You could say that it's climbing.

Cameron: Rising.

Beatriz: You could say it's not dropping because the temperature is moving up.

Teacher: What about the line for Hawaii?

Zhang: Hawaii doesn't really change.

Arthur: It is plain.

Zhang: It is steady and it's around the 80s.

Beatriz: But it's not steady because it still goes up and down a little.

Teacher: What does Zhang mean by *steady?* Could we say that it's steady if the temperature remains more or less the same, even if there is a little bit of change?

Gil: It's steady because it's always around the 70s or 80s. It's just changing a little bit.

The teacher helps students focus on the overall trend of the graph through gestures, drawing, and developing language. Many of the students are noticing the overall shape of the graph as increasing, decreasing or staying the same, despite weekly fluctuation. As Cameron comments on Keith's drawing of the line and Zhang and Beatriz discuss the meaning of *steady,* two important ideas become part of the conversation—that the graph shows many fluctuations of temperature in each location and that it also shows overall trends.

Dialogue Box

Temperatures Below Zero

In Session 1.3, students in this class are finding the difference between high and low temperatures for Churchill, Canada. They have determined that the highest temperature is 54°F and are considering how to read the lowest temperature, which is below zero. The teacher has drawn a vertical number line on the board with the two temperatures marked.

Teacher: What was the coolest temperature on the graph for Churchill, Canada?

Kelley: 23.

Teacher: Who remembers what we call the numbers below zero?

Kelley: They're called negative. Negative 23.

Murphy: I disagree. It's negative 18.

Deondra: Negative 22.

The teacher sketches a vertical number line, similar to a thermometer with the low and high temperatures for Churchill marked.

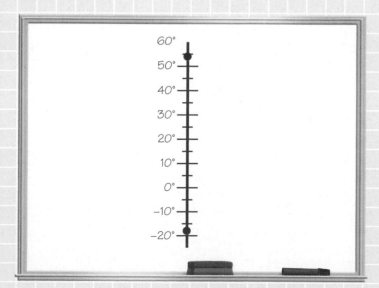

Teacher: Where is this point? What values is it between? What is it closer to?

Murphy: The negative 10 and the negative 20.

Kelley: It's closer to 20, and the line in the middle, the 15.

Gil: Do you mean negative 15?

Kelley: I mean negative 15.

Deondra: I think it's negative 22 because it's higher than the negative 20, so the number has to be higher.

Kenji: But it's closer to zero, so it's a lesser number.

Teacher: Is this point a little bit colder or a little bit warmer than negative 20?

Deondra: Warmer. . . . Oh, it would be closer to the zero, because it's warmer.

Elena: I think it's negative 18 because it's a little bit warmer than negative 20.

Teacher: But I'm still seeing some puzzled looks. If it's 20 degrees out—*positive* 20 degrees—and it starts getting colder and colder, what are the temperatures? Look where I'm pointing—what do you think the temperature is?

The teacher points successively at 20°, 15°, 10°, 5°, 0°, –5°, –10°, and –15°. Students say the temperatures as she points.

Beatriz: It's going *down*. It's like five below zero, ten below zero, 15 below zero.

Dwayne: It's like it's going up but it's going down because the minus is saying "below zero."

Keisha: Negative 18 should be between negative 10 and negative 20.

Gil: And that line means negative 15. So it goes in between that and negative 20.

Teacher: What is the difference between the hottest and coldest temperatures? How can you think about it? What if we start at the negative 18—how far is it to positive 54?

Kenji: We could plus 18 because that would get us to zero.

Teacher: So you added 18 to negative 18 to get to zero.

Benjamin: Then you need another 54 degrees to get up to the 54.

The teacher writes on the board:

$$-18° + 18° = 0°$$

$$0° + 54° = 54°$$

Teacher: What is the difference between the coldest and warmest temperatures? How much did the temperature change?

Gil: You have to add the 18 and the 54 because that's how far it is on the number line.

Kelley: 54 plus 10 is 64. Then you plus another 8, and it's 72. So it changed 72 degrees.

To help students think about the meaning of the values below zero on the number line, the teacher asks students to consider whether this temperature is warmer or colder than 0°, −10°, and −20°. Zero degrees is an important reference point as students determine the difference between 54° and −18°.

Dialogue Box

Where Are the Greens? Blues? Reds?

In Session 2.2, the students have listed the numbers for the first 10 green cubes in the red-blue-green repeating pattern.

Teacher: What did you notice about the green numbers?

Jane: They are all counting by three numbers.

Teacher: Why do you say that?

Jane: Because you skip two and then the one you land on is the counting by three number.

Keisha: Each pattern group has three in it.

Teacher: What is that called?

Denzel: A unit.

Oscar: It also works because it is the third color. It is like we are counting 1, 2, 3, 1, 2, 3.

Teacher: Let me ask you a question. What color would the 36th cube be? Put a thumb up when you think you know.

[Many thumbs go up very quickly. The teacher waits a few more seconds.]

Teacher: Many of you are pretty sure about the 36th cube, even though you didn't figure that one out on your student sheet. Why?

Keith: 36 is just two more threes, 30, 33, 36.

Jung: 36 is a multiple of three, so every third cube is on a three, so green works for 36. Counting by three numbers are green.

In Session 2.3, the class looks at the three number sequences for red, blue, and green. The teacher asks students to look at the three lists of numbers and talk about what they notice and how they think the number sequences are related.

Teacher: Did anyone notice anything about the three lists of numbers? What about the blue list?

Adam: If it's a blue, you say 2, 5, 8, 11, then 14, and you keep going.

Benjamin: It's just a three pattern starting with two.

Becky: It is green minus one is blue.

Teacher: There are many ideas here. First of all, Benjamin is saying that it's a three pattern starting with two. Who else can say something about Benjamin's idea?

Jane: If it was a regular 3s pattern, it would go 3, 6. But this pattern starts on two, but it's by 3s because there are three more to get to each blue, except for the first blue.

Elena: He is saying that it is counting by 3s except not starting at three.

Teacher: Are you saying that for 2, 5, 8, 11, you are still counting by 3s?

Students: Yes, and the red list is going by 3s, too.

Murphy: At the end, I just kept looking at my blue sheet to do the reds.

Teacher: How did you do that?

Murphy: See, the first blue minus one is red. So the first red is one.

Jung: I did the same thing, except I used the green and blue. I used the green to help with blue and the blue to help with red.

Teacher: This reminds me that at the beginning of this discussion, Becky was saying that green minus one is blue. Who has some ideas about what Becky means by that?

Jane: Because the blue is one before the green and green is one after blue.

Cameron: Can I show it on the board? [Cameron comes up to the list of numbers.] See, this is a three (on the green list) and this is a two (on the blue list), so three minus one is two. And this is a six and this is a five, and this is a nine and this is an eight. It's minus one every time.

In these two excerpts from Sessions 2.2 and 2.3, the class is noticing that each of the three number sequences increases by three. Sometimes students think that the number sequence for blue is counting by 2s because it starts with two. The idea that you can count by 3s starting at different numbers may be a new idea for some students.

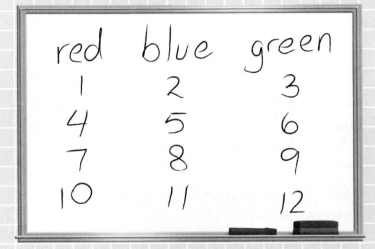

red	blue	green
1	2	3
4	5	6
7	8	9
10	11	12

Dialogue Box

"He's Taking Bigger Steps, So He'll Catch Up"

At the beginning of Session 3.2, this class is describing and comparing how Franick's and Bolar's marbles increase over 30 days. The teacher asks what students notice about how Franick's and Bolar's total marbles change during the first week.

	DAY	FRANICK	BOLAR
	Beginning	30	0
Week 1	Day 1	33	5
	Day 2	36	10
	Day 3	39	15
	Day 4	42	20
	Day 5	45	25
	Day 6	48	30
	Day 7	51	35
Week 2	Day 8		
	Day 9		
	Day 10		

Jung: Franick had 30 from leftovers.

Ines: Franick started with 30 and added three each day.

Denzel: Bolar started with zero and five were added each day.

Bridget: Franick had 30 marbles more than Bolar. And then at the end, Bolar has 30 more than Franick. (Bridget is referring to the totals on Day 30.)

Kim: Bolar catches up.

Teacher: What about the first week? Do you see Bolar catching up?

Murphy: I notice that each night Bolar gets at least the same as Franick because every day he gets closer to what Franick has. On Night 7, he's not as far as Night 1.

Teacher: Will that pattern continue happening?

Kelley: He'll have more than Franick.

Denzel: Five is more than three, so he's going to have more than Franick.

Gil: He's taking bigger steps, so he'll catch up.

Elena: The kind of pace Franick's taking is slower than what Bolar has because of the five. He'll quickly catch up and pass Franick.

Teacher: What happens in the second week? [They quickly fill in the numbers for Week 2.]

Cameron: On Day 14, Bolar had 70 and Franick had 72, so he was just two away.

Elena: On Day 15, they both have 75 marbles. And after that, Bolar has more.

Bridget: And also, the difference between five and three is two.

Teacher: What do you mean, the difference between five and three? Why is that important?

Bridget: The difference between what they get is two.

Teacher: So each night Franick gets three and Bolar gets five? And why is the two important?

Kelley: The difference keeps counting by 2s.

Gil: On Day 14, Franick is in the lead with two more and on Day 13, she has four more, and on Day 12 she has six more.

The teacher records what Gil is saying like this:

	Franick	Bolar	Difference
Day 12	66	60	6
Day 13	69	65	4
Day 14	72	70	2
Day 15	75	75	0

Teacher: Elena said they were tied on Day 15, with 75 marbles each. Then Gil was going backward from Day 15 and noticing that the differences get bigger.

Murphy: It keeps on. If you look at the 2s thing, it keeps on going back.

Teacher: If you look at it going forward, what is happening?

Nancy: Franick was winning at first and then Bolar won because he had a bigger number he got each night.

The students are noticing an important feature of the comparison between Franick and Bolar. Although Franick starts out with 30 more marbles, Bolar accumulates marbles at a higher rate (five marbles per night) than Franick (three marbles per night). Bridget and Kelley point out that Bolar receives two more marbles per night than Franick. Over time, this accumulation of two more per night brings Bolar's total closer and closer to Franick's until he finally has more marbles. Students are noticing more than just the total number of marbles; they are noticing the rate of change (number of marbles per day) and that the difference between the rates for Franick and Bolar is two. As Kelley says, "the difference keeps counting by 2s." Students are noticing the rate of change as they look at the table, and they will also see this rate, and the difference between rates, as represented in graphs, starting in Session 3.4.

Dialogue Box

Why Are There Five 2s?

In Session 3.2, the class is discussing how to find the number of marbles for Tovar on Day 10.

Teacher: Close your eyes and think about Tovar. He had 20 marbles from the year before and he got two Magic Marbles nightly. How could you figure out how many marbles Tovar had on the 10th day without figuring out every day from one to nine?

Nicholas: Two times ten, that's 20. I think that's right.

Teacher: So he had 20 on the 10th day?

Nicholas: No, wait . . .

Keisha: He had 20 leftovers.

Teacher: What are you going to do with those 20?

Keisha: Add it to the 20. 20 plus 20 is 40.

Adam: Because he had 20 marbles from the year before.

The teacher sketches on the board a table showing Tovar's accumulation of marbles. She adds a column to record the calculations students are using to find the total for a particular day.

DAY	TOVAR	
Beginning amount	20	
5	30	
10	40	$(2 \times 10) + 20 = 40$
15		
20		

Teacher: What about the 15th day?

Denzel: Tovar already has 40 so you do five times two, which is ten marbles, and you add it, so it's 50.

Teacher: First of all, do you think it's correct? And, second, where do you think the five times two came from?

Nancy: The five came from adding five more days on to her days, and two marbles per day.

Teacher: Where's the 20 that Tovar started out with? I don't see any 20.

Zhang: Because Keisha already had 40. She added on already to get 40, so Denzel didn't have to because she used his 40.

The teacher records their thinking on the chart.

DAY	TOVAR	
Beginning amount	20	
5	30	
10	40	$(2 \times 10) + 20 = 40$
15	50	$40 + (5 \times 2) = 50$
20		

Pilar: Every five days you have to times it by two, so we're adding 10.

Teacher: I have a question and you can't use your sheet, so turn it over. We know that Tovar has 20 marbles at the beginning and receives two each night. If we want to know how many marbles he has on the fifth day, is there a way to figure that out without looking at your table? Think about it and put up a thumb quietly when you are ready.

[After a minute, many students have their thumbs up. The teacher asks for responses.]

Dwayne: 30, because I counted by two, for five days— 22, 24, 26, 28, 30.

Elena: First I knew it was 20, so I did 2, 4, 6, 8, 10, and then I did 20 + 10 = 30.

Teacher: Pretend for a moment that Tovar had no leftover marbles from last year. He starts with zero, and he gets two marbles each night. How many marbles on Day 5?

Jung: Ten. Because you are counting by 2s five times.

Teacher: It's counting by 2s five times? There is a math way to say that. How are the two, the five, and the ten related?

Oscar: It's kind of like two times five. Because two times five is ten.

Teacher: Why did we use five? Why are there five 2s?

Keisha: Because that's how many he got in five days.

Jung: Every five days he gets ten.

Teacher: He got two marbles every day for five days, so that's five groups of two. I could write 5×2. What if we were on Day 17? How many 2s would I need to count up all of Tovar's marbles?

In this conversation, Denzel, Nancy, and Zhang first add on to a previous total in order to find a new total. For example, for Day 15, they use the total for Day 10 and add on ten more. The teacher is thinking about how to help students develop a general rule for any day—a rule that would not depend on knowing the total for some previous day. To do this, she temporarily eliminates the beginning amount of marbles so that students can concentrate on how the number of days relates to the total number of marbles. She is also intending to use what students say to help students see that multiplication is useful in this situation. After this discussion, she has them return to work on finding a rule for the number of marbles Tovar has on any day, now including the beginning amount of 20 marbles.

Using Graphs to Compare Situations with a Constant Rate of Change

In Session 3.6, students are discussing the graphs they have made. One graph compares Tovar and Winger, the second compares Tovar and Gowen, and the third compares Tovar and Lazik. The teacher first asks students to describe what is happening in the Tovar and Lazik graph.

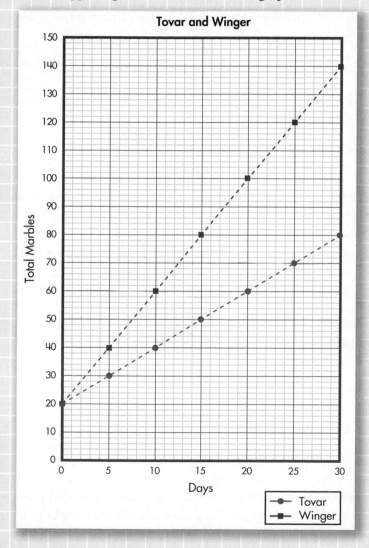

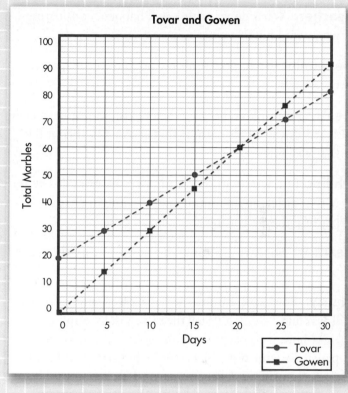

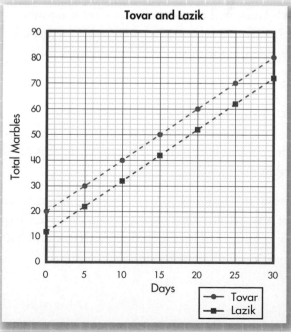

Edwin: They're mainly going the same, going the same path together.

Benjamin: Tovar's graph is higher, but I don't know if Lazik will ever connect with Tovar.

Teacher: What do you think will happen, considering what you know?

Benjamin: Right now probably no, but in the future, maybe yes.

Beatriz: I think no because they've always just been eight apart for the whole path. If that carries on, then it'll be that way forever.

Philip: I disagree with Benjamin because even if they start with a different amount, it's never going to change because they're getting the same amount.

Teacher: So we're assuming they keep getting the same number of marbles each day.

Nancy: For Lazik, I think she has a lower number than Tovar and I think it'll stay the same distance apart because right now, if you kept the graph going, it'll shoot off the paper the same way. [Nancy holds her arms parallel to show how they would continue in the same way.]

Oscar: Lazik will never catch up to Tovar because if your brother's in the second grade and you're in third, he'll never catch up with you.

Jung: He could skip a grade.

Oscar: Yeah, but that's what I'm saying. If it keeps going the same, he'll be in third grade, fourth grade, fifth grade, but you'll be in fourth, fifth, sixth. They'll always be eight marbles apart.

Teacher: If Tovar and Gowen's graph continued in the same way—Tovar kept getting two and Gowen kept getting three marbles every night—what would happen?

Elena: Whenever Gowen gets more, Tovar will get more too, but not as many.

Cameron: I think it's going to go out if you keep going.

Teacher: What do you mean, Cameron—can you show us on the graph?

[Cameron shows with his hands how the distance between the two lines on the graph will become greater and greater.]

Keith: I thought before we had this graph, Tovar would be ahead of Gowen, but then I saw that Gowen starts at zero but he gets more. Now I think he'd get lots more.

Teacher: When would he get lots more?

Keith: If it keeps going, he gets more and more, and Tovar can never catch up.

Keisha: After they cross, it's like the Tovar and Winger graph—the space between them gets bigger and bigger.

Kim: For Tovar and Winger in the future, Winger is going to get more and more and Tovar is going to get more, too, but not as much. [She goes up to the graph.] For Winger, it's going to be higher, and for Tovar, more over to the side [she gestures to show Winger's points on the graph increasing along a steeper line than Tovar's].

Adam: Winger's getting double Tovar because Tovar gets two and Winger gets four, so they're not going to meet again.

Ines: I think Winger's always going to be ahead of Tovar and Tovar's always going to be ahead of Lazik, but Tovar and Gowen kind of confuses me. It looks different. They cut in half. In Tovar and Winger, Winger is so much more ahead.

Teacher: You know how Oscar gave us an example about grades for Tovar and Lazik? A story like that might help us understand Tovar and Gowen better.

Tovar and Lazik have different starting amounts but acquire marbles at the same rate. Oscar visualizes this comparison as the difference between two students who are a grade apart; if they each advance one grade per year, they will always be one grade apart. Most of the students in the class are convinced that Tovar and Lazik will always be eight marbles apart and that Tovar's and Winger's totals will continue to get farther and farther apart. However, not all third graders believe that they can know what will happen on a part of the graph that has not yet been drawn. For example, Benjamin is not as convinced as some of his classmates: "Right now probably no, but in the future, maybe yes." He may be thinking about what could happen in a real

situation—perhaps the children will get a different number of marbles. His confusion may be mathematical: he may not be visualizing how the difference between two quantities stays the same if the same amount is added to each. It is not unusual for third graders to have the most difficulty understanding the comparison between Tovar and Gowen, as Ines does. The teacher suggests that the class think about a story to help them visualize this situation. For example, they may think about two brothers, one shorter than the other, but the first brother grows more quickly, surpassing the second in height. Keep in mind that comparing different rates of change is a new experience for third graders. They will continue working with these ideas in Grade 4.

Student Math Handbook

The *Student Math Handbook* pages related to this unit are pictured on the following pages. This book is designed to be used flexibly: as a resource for students doing classwork, as a book students can take home for reference while doing homework and playing math games with their families, and as a reference for families to better understand the work their children are doing in class.

When students take the *Student Math Handbook* home, they and their families can discuss these pages together to reinforce or enhance students' understanding of the mathematical concepts and games in this unit.

▲ Math Words and Ideas, p. 42

Math Words and Ideas

Skip Counting

Math Words
• skip counting
• multiples

This 100 chart shows skip counting by 3s.
The shaded numbers are multiples of 3.

1	2	3	4	5	6	7	8	9	10
11	12	13	14	15	16	17	18	19	20
21	22	23	24	25	26	27	28	29	30
31	32	33	34	35	36	37	38	39	40
41	42	43	44	45	46	47	48	49	50
51	52	53	54	55	56	57	58	59	60
61	62	63	64	65	66	67	68	69	70
71	72	73	74	75	76	77	78	79	80
81	82	83	84	85	86	87	88	89	90
91	92	93	94	95	96	97	98	99	100

$10 \times 3 = 30$

Cubes stacked in groups of 3 also show skip counting by 3s.

3 6 9 12 15 18 21 24 27 30 $10 \times 3 = 30$

A number line can also show skip counting.

0 3 6 9 12 15 18 21 24 27 30 $10 \times 3 = 30$

42 forty-two

▲ Math Words and Ideas, p. 66

Math Words and Ideas

What's the Temperature?

(page 1 of 4)

Math Words
• Celsius
• degree
• Fahrenheit

How warm or cold is it outside? You can find out by using a thermometer to measure the temperature.

Temperature is measured in two different scales: degrees Fahrenheit and degrees Celsius.

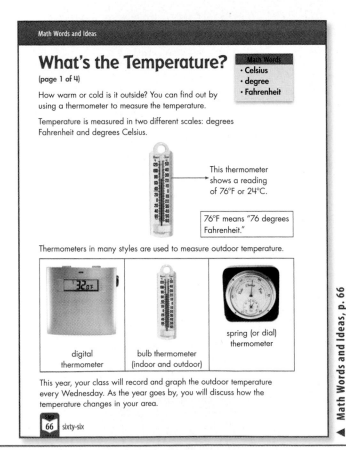

This thermometer shows a reading of 76°F or 24°C.

76°F means "76 degrees Fahrenheit."

Thermometers in many styles are used to measure outdoor temperature.

digital thermometer

bulb thermometer (indoor and outdoor)

spring (or dial) thermometer

This year, your class will record and graph the outdoor temperature every Wednesday. As the year goes by, you will discuss how the temperature changes in your area.

66 sixty-six

▲ Math Words and Ideas, p. 67

Math Words and Ideas

What's the Temperature?

(page 2 of 4)

This map shows the temperature in degrees Fahrenheit across the United States for a day in September.

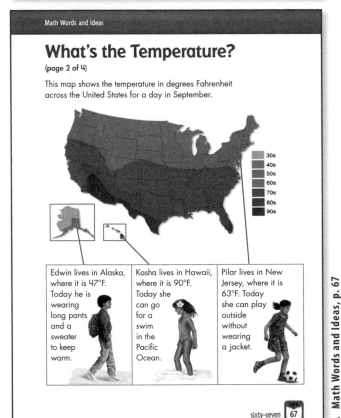

30s
40s
50s
60s
70s
80s
90s

Edwin lives in Alaska, where it is 47°F. Today he is wearing long pants and a sweater to keep warm.

Kasha lives in Hawaii, where it is 90°F. Today she can go for a swim in the Pacific Ocean.

Pilar lives in New Jersey, where it is 63°F. Today she can play outside without wearing a jacket.

sixty-seven 67

What's the Temperature?
(page 3 of 4)

The average temperature in Anchorage, Alaska for the month of March is 26°F.

The record high for March is 51°F (set in 1984).

The record low for March is −24°F (set in 1971).

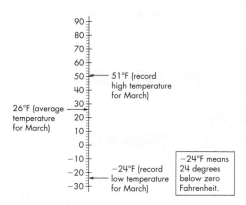

26°F (average temperature for March)

51°F (record high temperature for March)

−24°F (record low temperature for March)

−24°F means 24 degrees below zero Fahrenheit.

 What is the difference between the record high (51°F) and the record low (−24°F)?

68 sixty-eight

▲ Math Words and Ideas, p. 68

What's the Temperature?
(page 4 of 4)

Here is the temperature graph from Keith's class at the end of September.

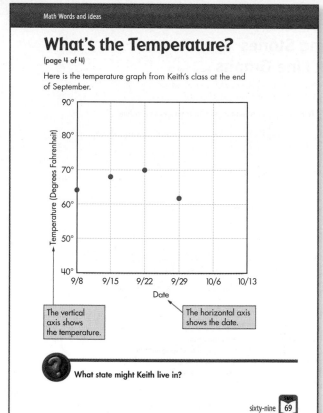

The vertical axis shows the temperature.

The horizontal axis shows the date.

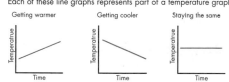 What state might Keith live in?

sixty-nine 69

▲ Math Words and Ideas, p. 69

Reading Points on a Line Graph

Each point on this graph represents two connected pieces of information, the date and the temperature.

For example, look at the point marked with a star (☆) on the graph.

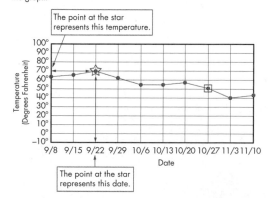

The point at the star represents this temperature.

The point at the star represents this date.

The point marked with a star (☆) shows that on September 22 the temperature was 70°F.

 What does the point marked with a square (□) tell you?

70 seventy

▲ Math Words and Ideas, p. 70

Telling Stories from Line Graphs (page 1 of 2)

Each of these line graphs represents part of a temperature graph.

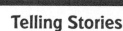

Getting warmer　Getting cooler　Staying the same

Here is a complete temperature graph for one spring day.

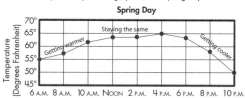

Spring Day

Kathryn wrote this story about the weather on the spring day represented on the graph.

When I woke up it was cloudy and cool. By noon the sun came out and it was warm enough to play outside. In the evening it got cooler and I needed an extra blanket to sleep that night.

 What is the highest temperature? What is the lowest temperature? What is the difference between the highest and lowest temperatures?

seventy-one 71

▲ Math Words and Ideas, p. 71

Math Words and Ideas

Telling Stories from Line Graphs (page 2 of 2)

This line graph shows how the temperature changed in Anchorage, Alaska over time from January to June.

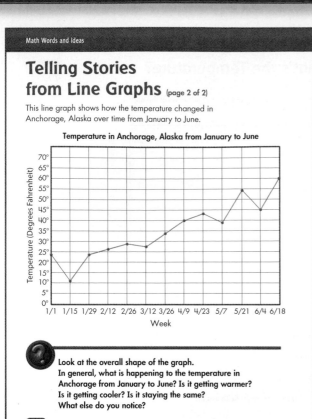

Temperature in Anchorage, Alaska from January to June

(y-axis: Temperature (Degrees Fahrenheit), values 0° to 70° in 5° increments)
(x-axis: Week — 1/1, 1/15, 1/29, 2/12, 2/26, 3/12, 3/26, 4/9, 4/23, 5/7, 5/21, 6/4, 6/18)

Look at the overall shape of the graph.
In general, what is happening to the temperature in Anchorage from January to June? Is it getting warmer? Is it getting cooler? Is it staying the same?
What else do you notice?

72 seventy-two

▲ Math Words and Ideas, p. 72

Math Words and Ideas

Repeating Patterns (page 1 of 2)

Math Words
· unit

Here are some repeating patterns made with connecting cubes.

The unit is the part of the pattern that repeats over and over.

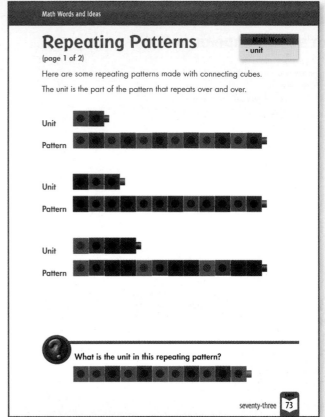

Unit

Pattern

Unit

Pattern

Unit

Pattern

What is the unit in this repeating pattern?

seventy-three **73**

▲ Math Words and Ideas, p. 73

Math Words and Ideas

Repeating Patterns (page 2 of 2)

In this repeating pattern, each cube is numbered.

1st orange cube   2nd orange cube   3rd orange cube

1 2 3 4 5 6 7 8 9 10 . . .

In this pattern the first orange cube is cube 3.

The second orange cube is cube 6.

The third orange cube is cube 9.

When a pattern repeats, you can use what you know to figure out what will come next.

If this pattern continues in the same way, will the fifteenth cube be yellow or orange? How do you know? What color will the thirty-first cube be? How do you know? What number is matched with the sixth orange cube? How do you know?

74 seventy-four

▲ Math Words and Ideas, p. 74

Math Words and Ideas

The Magic Marbles of Rhomaar (page 1 of 6)

A Situation of Constant Change

On the planet Rhomaar, children receive Magic Marbles as gifts. The children on Rhomaar can use these Magic Marbles to buy toys, books, snacks, and other things they like.

For the first 30 nights of each year, each child on Rhomaar is visited by a Magic Marble Messenger, who leaves that child the same number of Magic Marbles each night. On the first night of the year, the children find out how many marbles they will receive each night for 30 nights. This number can be different for different Rhomaarian children.

The Magic Marbles are so valuable that many children do not use all their Magic Marbles in any one year and may save some for the next year. So every year, some children start with leftover marbles and some do not.

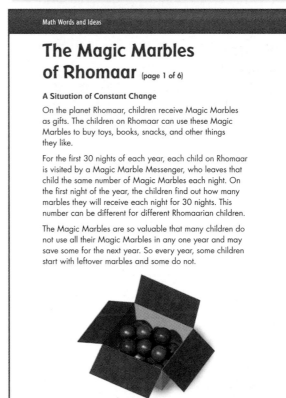

seventy-five **75**

▲ Math Words and Ideas, p. 75

Math Words and Ideas

The Magic Marbles of Rhomaar (page 2 of 6)

A Situation of Constant Change, *continued*

Leeyan lives on the planet Rhomaar. She has saved 10 marbles from last year. On the first night of the year, she receives 2 marbles. Leeyan continues to receive 2 marbles each night for the first 30 nights of the year.

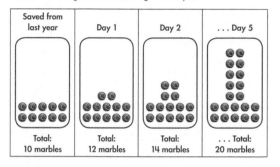

Saved from last year	Day 1	Day 2	. . . Day 5
Total: 10 marbles	Total: 12 marbles	Total: 14 marbles	. . . Total: 20 marbles

▲ Math Words and Ideas, p. 76

Math Words and Ideas

The Magic Marbles of Rhomaar (page 3 of 6)

How Many Marbles?

Leeyan had 10 Magic Marbles left from the year before. She was given 2 Magic Marbles each night for 30 nights. How many marbles does Leeyan have on the tenth day?

10 days
× 2 marbles per day

20 marbles

+ 10 marbles from last year

30 total marbles on the tenth day

How many marbles does Leeyan have on the twelfth day? How did you figure that out?

▲ Math Words and Ideas, p. 77

Math Words and Ideas

The Magic Marbles of Rhomaar (page 4 of 6)

Math Words
- table
- column
- row

Looking at a Table

A table is a way to organize information.

Leeyan had 10 Magic Marbles left from the year before. She was given 2 Magic Marbles each night for 30 nights.

This table shows how many marbles Leeyan has after every 5 days.

Columns go up and down.

Rows go across.

Beginning here, the table skips some rows.

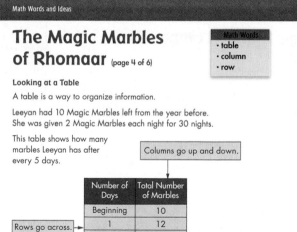

Number of Days	Total Number of Marbles
Beginning	10
1	12
2	14
3	16
4	18
5	20
10	30
15	?

This row shows that, after the fifth day, Leeyan has 20 marbles.

How many marbles does Leeyan have on the fifteenth day? How did you figure that out?

▲ Math Words and Ideas, p. 78

Math Words and Ideas

The Magic Marbles of Rhomaar (page 5 of 6)

Looking at a Table, *continued*

Leeyan had 10 Magic Marbles left from the year before. She was given 2 Magic Marbles each night for 30 nights.

This table shows how many marbles Leeyan has after every 5 days.

Number of Days	Total Number of Marbles
Beginning	10
5	20
10	30
15	40
20	50
25	60
30	?

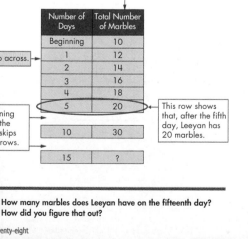

This row shows that, after the twentieth day, Leeyan will have 50 marbles.

How many marbles does Leeyan have on the thirtieth day? How did you figure that out?

▲ Math Words and Ideas, p. 79

Math Words and Ideas

The Magic Marbles of Rhomaar (page 6 of 6)

Looking at a Graph

Leeyan had 10 Magic Marbles left from the year before.
She was given 2 Magic Marbles each night for 30 nights.

Here is a graph that shows Leeyan's growing collection of marbles.

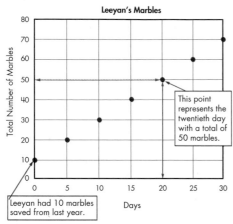

This point represents the twentieth day with a total of 50 marbles.

Leeyan had 10 marbles saved from last year.

Why do you think the points on the graph are in a straight line?

▲ Math Words and Ideas, p. 80

Math Words and Ideas

Magic Marble Comparisons

(page 1 of 6)

Leeyan had 10 Magic Marbles left from the year before.
She was given 2 Magic Marbles each night for 30 nights.

Sujo had no Magic Marbles left from the year before.
She was given 2 Magic Marbles each night for 30 nights.

Will we ever have the same number of marbles on the same day?

Day	Leeyan	Sujo
Beginning	10	0
Day 5	20	10
Day 10	30	20
Day 15	40	30
Day 20	50	40
Day 25	60	50
Day 30	70	60

▲ Math Words and Ideas, p. 81

Math Words and Ideas

Magic Marble Comparisons

(page 2 of 6)

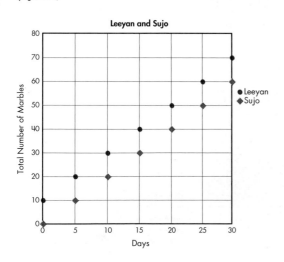

Leeyan and Sujo

● Leeyan
◆ Sujo

If Leeyan and Sujo keep getting 2 marbles each for 30 more nights, will they ever have the same number of marbles on the same day? How does the table show that? How does the graph show that?

▲ Math Words and Ideas, p. 82

Math Words and Ideas

Magic Marble Comparisons

(page 3 of 6)

Leeyan had 10 Magic Marbles left from the year before.
She was given 2 Magic Marbles each night for 30 nights.

Marzig also had 10 Magic Marbles left from the year before.
He was given 3 Magic Marbles each night for 30 nights.

Will we ever have the same number of marbles on the same day again after the beginning of the year?

Day	Leeyan	Marzig
Beginning	10	10
Day 5	20	25
Day 10	30	40
Day 15	40	55
Day 20	50	70
Day 25	60	85
Day 30	70	100

▲ Math Words and Ideas, p. 83

Magic Marble Comparisons
(page 4 of 6)

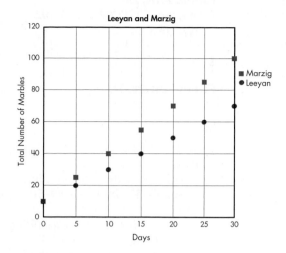

Leeyan and Marzig

■ Marzig
● Leeyan

 If Leeyan keeps getting 2 marbles each night and Marzig keeps getting 3 marbles each night for 30 more nights, will they ever have the same number of marbles on the same day? How does the table show that? How does the graph show that?

▲ Math Words and Ideas, p. 84

Magic Marble Comparisons
(page 5 of 6)

Leeyan had 10 Magic Marbles left from the year before. She was given 2 Magic Marbles each night for 30 nights.

Bethin had no Magic Marbles left from the year before. She was given 3 Magic Marbles each night for 30 nights.

Do we ever have the same number of marbles on the same day?

Day	Leeyan	Bethin
Beginning	10	0
Day 5	20	15
Day 10	30	30
Day 15	40	45
Day 20	50	60
Day 25	60	75
Day 30	70	90

▲ Math Words and Ideas, p. 85

Magic Marble Comparisons
(page 6 of 6)

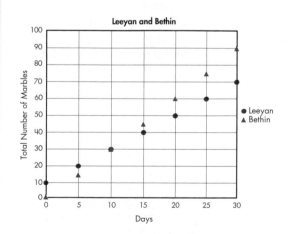

Leeyan and Bethin

● Leeyan
▲ Bethin

 Do Leeyan and Bethin ever have the same number of marbles on the same day? How does the table show that? How does the graph show that? If Leeyan keeps getting 2 marbles each night and Bethin keeps getting 3 marbles each night for 30 more nights, will they ever have the same number of marbles on the same day again? How do you know?

▲ Math Words and Ideas, p. 86

Writing Rules to Describe Change

Tharna had 5 Magic Marbles left from the year before. She was given 3 Magic Marbles each night for 30 nights. How many marbles does Tharna have on the tenth day?

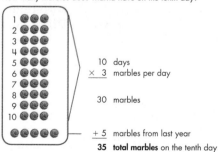

10 days
× 3 marbles per day

30 marbles

+ 5 marbles from last year
35 total marbles on the tenth day

Tharna wrote this rule about her marbles.

I multiply the number of days by 3 marbles per day, and then add on the 5 marbles that I had left from last year. That tells me the number of marbles I have on any day.

Number of Days × 3 + 5

 Does Tharna's rule work for the total number of marbles on the tenth day? Can you use Tharna's rule to find out how many marbles she will have on the thirtieth day? Make a table or a graph of Tharna's marbles to check.

▲ Math Words and Ideas, p. 87

Index